Despite not being born an Islander, few would doubt Oliver Frazer's credentials for tackling so immense a subject as this remarkable survey of the Isle of Wight's natural history. He joined the Isle of Wight Archaeological and Natural History Society more than fifty years ago, and served as its President in the 1960s.

Oliver Frazer was born and educated at Dulwich, south-east London, and from an early age showed an interest in natural history. He came to live on the Island in 1936 and has lived here ever since, except for the period of the Second World War, when he served in the Glider Pilot Regiment in the invasion of Normandy on D-Day and at Arnhem. It was here that, having dug himself a slit-trench for his Bren Gun position, as darkness fell, he was intrigued to find that the roots protruding from the side of the trench were brightly luminous, giving enough light to read by. He put a portion of the root in the top pocket of his battle-dress and resumed the battle. On his safe return, he sent the root to the British Museum (Natural History) and had a most interesting reply from the then Keeper of Botany, stating that the root was infected by the Honey Fungus, *Armillaria mellea*, which naturally started another interest, in fungi, which has persisted to this day.

Following the war, he trained as a teacher, specialising in biology and general science, in which subjects he had a successful career in island schools. He also took evening classes for the Workers' Educational Association on Natural History in the Isle of Wight, which proved extremely popular. He produced a series of radio broadcasts for Radio Solent entitled "What's in a Habitat", which was later produced as an educational pack, containing film-strips and commentaries on cassettes, with other support material, which has been much used by local and visiting schools.

He and his wife, Dorothy, who shares the same interests, have lived at Mottistone Mill, Brighstone, for many years, surrounded by wildlife.

Frontispiece
Family of Barn Owls, *Tyto alba*, in their tree
(photograph, Colin Fairweather).

The Natural History of
the Isle of Wight

Oliver Frazer

THE DOVECOTE PRESS

To members, past and present, of the Isle of Wight
Natural History and Archaeological Society,
to whom I owe so much

First published in 1990 by The Dovecote Press Ltd
Stanbridge, Wimborne, Dorset BH21 4JD

© Oliver Frazer 1990

Photoset in Palatino by The Typesetting Bureau Ltd, Wimborne, Dorset
Origination by Chroma Graphics (Overseas) Pte Ltd, Singapore
Printed and bound by Kim Hup Lee Printing Co Pte Ltd, Singapore

British Library Catalogue in Publication Data
Frazer, Oliver
The natural history of the Isle of Wight.
1. England. Natural history
1. Title
508.42

ISBN 0-946159-83-1

Contents

*The 16 pages of colour photographs illustrating
the Habitats are between pages 96 and 97*

Foreword

My first encounter with the Isle of Wight was quite dramatic. I was returning to this country after having spent four years in New Zealand, when our ship ran into a thick mist in Christchurch Bay, and we cautiously approached the Needles channel with the booming of many foghorns on every hand. We were all on deck peering out to catch our first glimpse of land, but nothing could be seen. At last, we could just make out the faint outlines of the Needles and Hurst Castle opposite, as we sailed between them and entered the Solent. It was then, as if by magic, that the mist lifted like a curtain, and the sun shone to reveal the Isle of Wight in all its glory. It was quite theatrical, and I shall never forget my first sight of the Island on that day in June, 1934. A patchwork of fields and hedges spread out before us with a backdrop of smooth rolling downs, with woods and fields, like lawns, coming down to the water's edge. It was like a garden. Not for nothing has it been called the Garden Isle. I have seen many ports in my sojourn round the world, many of them impressive and even awe-inspiring, but nowhere, absolutely nowhere, is there such a homely welcome as is afforded by the Isle of Wight as one approaches the port of Southampton.

I did not know at the time that my parents had already arranged for the family holiday to be spent at Freshwater in West Wight. We liked it so much that we went there again the next year, and my elder brother bought a house at Freshwater for my parents to retire to, and I came to live there as well. Apart from absence on war service, I have lived on the Island ever since. I was completely captivated, as my wife, whom I married after the war, came to be also.

I was fortunate in having a father who was himself a naturalist of considerable experience.

His main interest was in insects, and we did much field work together, but he encouraged me to take as wide an interest in wildlife as possible, rather than specialise in too narrow a field. One of the first things I did when I came to live on the Island was to join the Isle of Wight Natural History and Archaeological Society, an action for which I have been profoundly thankful ever since. This brought me into contact with many outstanding naturalists of many disciplines, who were always ready to share their knowledge, and, as time went on, I became more and more involved in the study of our local natural history. There is no end to the study of natural history, for the more one learns the more questions are posed that need an answer. It is time-consuming, but I can honestly say that for more than fifty years I have not had a single dull moment. There is always something of interest to be dealt with. Fortunately my wife shared my love of natural history, and we do everything together.

The Island is a wonderful place for the study of natural history, for it is so varied and yet so compact, that it provides more scope for study than anywhere of similar size on the mainland. I was fortunate to be a teacher of biology, which I largely approached through an interest in wildlife, so that my work and my hobby supported each other. My pupils, also were a great asset in carrying out fieldwork, I hope willingly, and in due course with the aid of other schools I was able to organise surveys of various kinds covering the whole Island, some of which are referred to in the following pages. There is no better way of learning than teaching, so the opportunity of taking W.E.A. evening classes on the Natural History of the Isle of Wight for 20 years taught me a lot. Unfortunately I had to give them up, owing to uncertain health.

I am most grateful for the opportunity to write this book. I look to it as a way of repaying my debt to all those who have helped me through the years, by imparting some of the knowledge I have gained for the benefit of others. Naturally much of the contents of this book will apply to other areas as well as the Isle of Wight, but that is no bad thing if it leads to a wider interest in natural history, wherever you may live. It is, however, essentially a book about the Island, and it is my fervent hope that those who read it will be resolved to find out more and, most importantly, do all they can to ensure that our priceless heritage is preserved for future generations.

OLIVER FRAZER
Mottistone

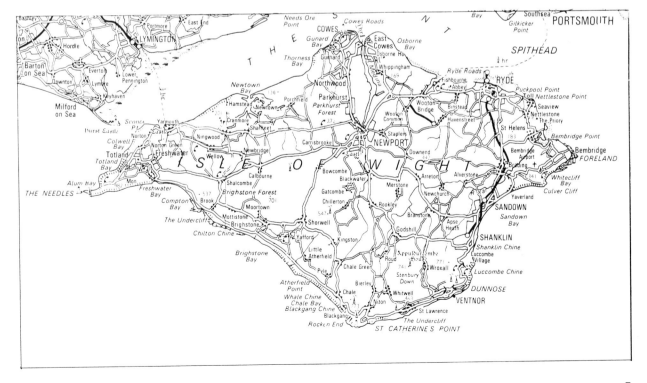

Introduction

'What's so special about the Isle of Wight, anyway?' That's a good question, and it requires a good answer. It is one of the main purposes of this book to provide that answer.

Having taken the trouble to cross that stretch of water that separates it from the mainland, you would expect the Island to be different, and so it is in a subtle and important way, which is not immediately apparent. With the exception of a number of specialities not found elsewhere in Britain, the plants and animals one encounters are the same as those on the mainland, so there are not likely to be many surprises there. What is important, however, is the variety of scenery in such a comparatively small area. Nowhere else does the scenery change so rapidly as one travels about, which is one of the reasons that coach tours are so popular. One is never far from the sea and there are unrivalled panoramic views of land and sea to be obtained, while at the same time there are intimate views of countryside features on every hand, as though in miniature. The truth is that the Island is a microcosm of the whole of south-east England. If you live in south-east England and come to the Island, you are sure to find somewhere which reminds you of home, for it is all here compressed and squeezed into an area which is less than one-tenth the size of Hampshire alone. This is the Island's secret, and, of course, this variety of scenery gives rise to a wide variety of different habitats, each with its own distinctive plants and animals, all clamouring for attention by the passing naturalist. Nowhere is there such a wide range of subjects for the pursuit of natural history as there is on the Isle of Wight.

There are basic geological reasons to account for the Island being a microcosm of south-east England, and these are explained in some detail in Chapter 1. Geology makes another important contribution to our study of natural history by means of the fossil record, which gives us an insight into the vital process of evolution resulting in the remarkable variety of plants and animals today.

Subsequent chapters present a general review of the plants and animals to be met with in the Island today. Where there are large numbers of species involved, care has been taken to avoid giving long lists of names, which can readily be found in other publications referred to in the text, if necessary. Attention is focussed on a few of the more interesting or important species concerned.

In the interests of accuracy, when first mentioned, the scientific name of a species is given, together with the common name, if it has one. Later on, only the common name may be given, once its identity has been properly established. Distribution maps of some species, where these are available, are provided alongside the text. In some cases these are based on one-kilometre

Map of the Isle of Wight showing Kilometre Grid.

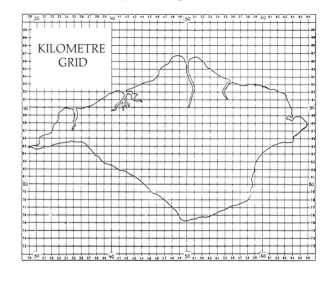

squares of the National Grid, of which 450 cover the Island. For the most part, however, the distribution maps are based on Tetrads, made up of four adjacent one-kilometre squares, so that there are 25 Tetrads to a ten-kilometre square on the National Grid. A total of 127 tetrads cover the Island. Unless otherwise stated, all records are post-1960, and records prior to 1970 are shown as open circles (○), while records post 1970 to 1989 are shown as closed circles (●). Where records obtained between 1960 and 1970 have not been confirmed in the twenty years from 1970 to 1989, it is reasonable to assume that there has been a reduction in population of that species in that area since 1970.

Reference is made on occasions to numbers of Red Data Book species. These are plant and animal species, which have been listed by the Nature Conservancy as belonging to one or other of a number of categories, e.g. Endangered, Vulnerable or Rare, according to the number of 10 kilometre squares in which they are found, and the severity of the threat of extinction. A further category, Nationally Scarce, comprises those species thought to occur in less than a hundred 10 kilometre squares in Great Britain.

· Part 2 contains a series of studies of particular habitats – Woodland, Downland, Farmland, Marshes and Ponds, Saltmarshes and Estuaries, Cliffs and Chines and the Seashore. In each case special consideration is given to the ways in

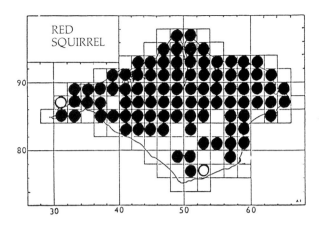

Map of the Isle of Wight showing distribution of the Red Squirrel on a tetrad grid.

which certain plants and animals benefit from the environment and adapt to the prevailing conditions, and how they affect each other. Each habitat study is accompanied by a page of coloured photographs depicting the plants and animals most closely associated with the habitat.

Finally, in Chapter 18, consideration is given to the future prospects of our wildlife in view of the ever increasing pressures from development, changing agricultural practices and recreational activities. A plea is made for more importance to be attached to the preservation of our wildlife and the countryside as our primary asset in attracting visitors and satisfying the needs of residents.

Acknowledgements

It is doubtful if anyone could write a book of this nature without directly or indirectly drawing on the knowledge of others. I am happy to acknowledge the considerable help that I have received from my many friends, mostly in the Isle of Wight Natural History and Archaeological Society, who have readily answered my questions and generally supported me with advice and encouragement and, in many cases, checked my manuscript for errors. I would particularly like to acknowledge the following for help in connection with the subjects shown in brackets after their names: Barry Angell (Butterflies), David Biggs (Galls and Bugs), Jim Cheverton (Birds and Dragonflies), Peter Cramp (Moths), Bill Farnham (Seaweeds), Roger Herbert (Marine Life), Jessica Holm (Squirrels), Allan Insole (Geology), Andy Keay (Arthropods), Ian Killeen (Molluscs), David Motkin, Editor of Proceedings, Colin Pope (Lichens), Richard Preece (Molluscs),

Derek Reid (Fungi), Bill Shepard (Botany and Beetles), Lorna Snow (Bryophytes), Ron Snow (Ants), John Stafford (Birds), Bob Stebbings (Bats) and David Tomalin, President of the Society.

Unless otherwise stated, the photographs are my own, taken over a number of years, but I acknowledge with gratitude those who kindly came to my rescue and lent me their own photographs to fill the gaps. Credit is duly given in the captions of the photographs and drawings concerned.

Unless otherwise stated, the diagrams and line drawings have been executed by my wife, Dorothy, while at the same time keeping me fed and watered during the preparation of this book, for which I am truly grateful.

Lastly, I am most indebted to my publisher, David Burnett, whose idea it originally was, and who has seen the whole project through to completion with exemplary patience and understanding.

PART 1

THE NATURAL HISTORY

Common Seal at Medina Valley Centre, Dodnor, in 1980
(photograph, Barbara Gibbons).

ONE

The Underlying Structure

It is important to realise, when engaged in the study of natural history, that one is, so to speak, coming in in the middle of the picture'. To have a proper understanding of the subject, therefore, it is necessary to know something about what has gone before. Hence the importance to us of the study of geology, which makes two important contributions to our subject:

1. The study of the arrangement of the rocks themselves helps us to understand the contour-forming processes, the formulation of soils and the underlying reasons for the present distribution of plants and animals in their various habitats.

2. The study of fossils in the rocks helps us to gain an insight into the vital process of evolution and the gradual development and increasing complexity of plant and animal life through the course of time, resulting in the remarkable variety of living things we have today: a process which, it must be remembered, is still going on and, it is hoped, will continue relentlessly into the future.

The Isle of Wight is well known for its remarkable variety of scenery and the wide range of plants and animals that are to be found in such a small area. It has been truly said that the Island is a microcosm of the whole of south-east England, and to understand the reasons for this it is necessary to reconstruct in one's own mind the manner in which the Island was made and how it has come to be the way it is. There have been three main stages:

1. DEPOSITION. All the rocks of which the Island is composed are sedimentary rocks, which have been deposited layer upon layer under water in varying situations, as shown in the accompanying diagram. The oldest rocks exposed on the surface are only about 120 million years old.

Diagram of Deposition showing the various strata laid down on the Island.

Recent evidence from boreholes and geophysical investigations made by oil companies has shown that older rocks are present underneath our feet. One would have to go further west, to Dorset, Devon and Cornwall, to see them at the surface. The oldest rocks that we can actually see are the Wessex and Vectis Formations, collectively grouped together as the Wealden Group. These muds and sands were laid down in a river valley which was gradually drowned by a shallow lagoon. On top of the wealden Group lie the Lower Greensand, Gault and Upper Greensand. This thick sequence of sandstones and mudstones were deposited under varying conditions in a shallow sea. These rocks were followed by the Chalk, the top of which marks the top of the local Cretaceous succession. About 65 million years ago, the whole area was uplifted and the upper layers of the Chalk were removed by erosion before the sea returned some 5 million years later. Over the next 30 million years or so, during the Palaeogene, sands and muds were laid down in the rivers, lagoons, deltas and shallow water along the coast of this sea. Finally, about 30 million years ago, earth movements caused another period of uplift and this part of the world became dry land, deposition of sediments ceased and erosion began.

2. UPLIFT (FOLDING). Earth movements continued for some 10 million years, buckling the rock layers into a series of folds across south-east England. These movements were associated with those which formed the Alps and the Pyrenees, some hundreds of kilometres to the south. The local folds all have the same form in profile, as indicated in the diagram. The southerly-facing slopes of the folds are gently inclined, while the northern slopes are almost vertical and highly compressed. The rock layers have thus been buckled into a series of step-like features. As the folds began to form, erosion began to strip away the central cores of the folds. The Island owes its shape and topography to the form and arrangements of these folds.

3. DENUDATION (EROSION). For over 20 million years the local land surface has been subject to weathering and erosion. Heat, frost, rain, wind and, more recently, the sea have moulded the landscape. The process operated fast on the softer rocks, so that the relatively hard Chalk and

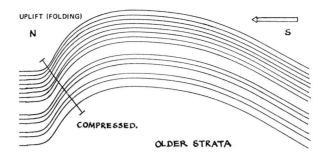

Diagram showing Uplift.

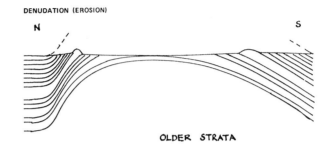

Diagram showing Denudation.

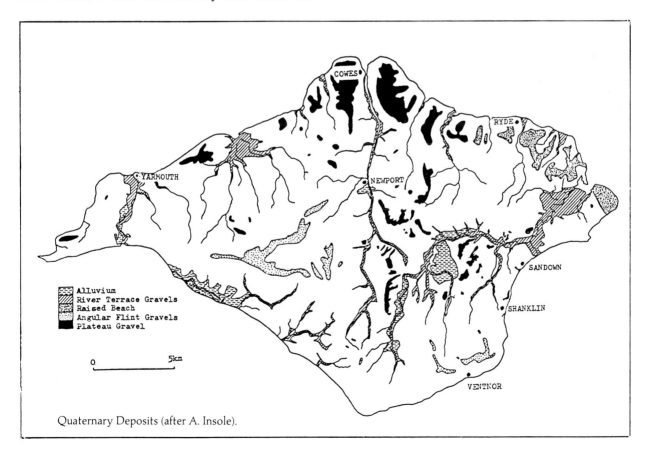

Quaternary Deposits (after A. Insole).

Upper Greensand now form hills, while the soft sands and mudstones underlie the lower ground, as is shown in the diagram. The process of erosion was greatest during the series of Ice Ages during the Pleistocene, which began about 2 million years ago, when there were alternate extremes of climatic conditions.

The rocks which comprise the Isle of Wight are the same as those found throughout southeast England, with the addition of the early Oligocene deposits, which are unique to the northern half of the Island. All these rocks are exposed within the small space of the Island, as can be seen in the accompanying geological map, and it is this which gives the Island its unique variety. If we take a section of the Island along the line AA1, as shown on the map, we can see how the denuded fold relates to the local topography of the Island. This pattern of a central Chalk ridge, where the strata are almost verti-

Simplified Geological map of the Isle of Wight, with insets showing cross-sections at AA1 and BB1 (see text above and opposite) (after A. Insole).

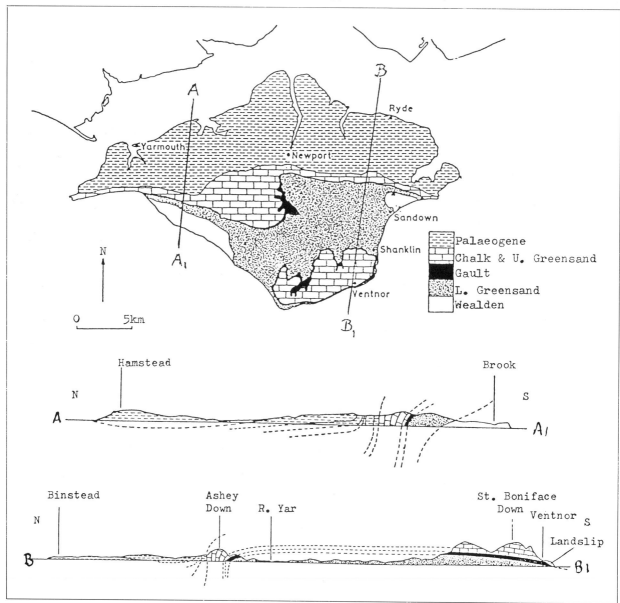

cal, with the older strata exposed to the south and the younger strata to the north, occurs throughout the length of the Island. If we project this central part of the pattern to the west, we can see it perfectly exposed in the vertical earliest Palaeogene strata comprising the famous coloured sands at Alum Bay, with the Chalk on the right and the younger Palaeogene deposits becoming horizontal on Headon Hill to the left. The same pattern, but as a mirror image, can be seen at Whitecliff Bay in the east.

If we take a section along the line BB1, as shown on the map, we see that the same pattern is repeated, but with the addition of another area of chalkland to the south, the remnant of the southern slope of the original fold. These are the downs at Shanklin, Ventnor and St Catherines, where the Lower Chalk and Upper Greensand overlie Gault clay. The latter, when lubricated by rain, leads to inevitable landslips, which are a feature of this area. Those at Ventnor and St Lawrence are comparatively stable, but those at Luccombe and at Blackgang are highly active.

That is not all, however, for, during the Pleistocene period, when most of the erosion took place, much of the eroded material was re-deposited in the form of various gravels on the old land surface and alluvium in the river valleys, as shown on the accompanying map. This serves to create an even greater diversity of soils and resulting habitats suitable for an even wider range of plants and animals.

So far as the fossil record is concerned, the Island has long since been regarded as classic ground. The crumbling cliffs of the Island have produced a remarkable range of fossils from the

Alum Bay, showing the almost vertical strata of the famous Coloured Sands. (Photograph, David Motkin).

Cretaceous period, through the Palaeogene to the Quaternary period. It is doubtful that any other place of equal size can boast of such a wide range of fossil evidence.

Starting with the Wealden, the oldest rocks of the Island are exposed in Brook Bay. The rocks to be seen at low tide here contain the partly petrified, partly carbonised, remains of pine logs which formed a log jam in the Wealden river some 120 million years ago. Up to a few years ago the outline of obvious pine logs could easily be discerned, but over-zealous collectors, together with natural erosion, have removed the best examples. As well as pines, the plants at this time included horsetails, ferns, tree-ferns and cycads, the cones of which are sometimes found. Generally speaking, however, the Wealden deposits do not contain many fossils, but what they lack in quantity they certainly make up for in quality, as it is here that the most important finds of several species of dinosaurs have been found. These are well represented in the Natural History Museum at Kensington, as well as the Museum of Isle of Wight Geology, which shares the same building as the County Library, Sandown, where footprints of the *Iguanodon*, preserved in stone slabs recovered

Gore Cliff, near Blackgang, the scene of a cliff-founder in 1928. (Photograph, Roger Smith for the National Trust)

Part of Pine Raft at Hanover Point, Brook, I.W. (Photograph, A. Insole).

from the beach, can also be seen.

As conditions changed from that of fresh water through lagoonal to marine conditions with the laying down of the Lower Greensand in a shallow sea, fossils of land-dwelling animals and plants gave way to marine organisms of the

Typical Ammonite from the Lower Greensand, about 100 million years old, and *(below)* an Ammonite in section, showing chambered interior.

Fossil Sea-urchin from the Upper Chalk, about 65 million years old.

time. Some of these, such as giant oysters, large triangular shaped molluscs known as *Mulletia mulleti*, branchiopods and the lobster, *Meyeria magna*, are locally common. One of the commonest and most familiar of all the fossils are the ammonites. They vary in size from minute spiral shells to enormous specimens too heavy to lift. The animal was rather like a cuttlefish or squid, and it lived in the end compartment of a chambered shell. It is presumed that the former compartments were filled with gas, so that the shell

acted as a float, while the animal dangled its tentacles in the water catching food as it drifted about. It had been a highly successful type of animal since its first appearance in Lower Jurassic times, some 50 million years previously, and yet it was due to become extinct, together with giant dinosaurs, by the time the Chalk was being laid down at the bottom of a deeper sea, marking the end of the Cretaceous Period. What brought about its extinction is a mystery, although it would have been an easy prey to predatory fish, such as sharks, which were increasing at that time. On the other hand, the closely related *Nautilus*, which had an even longer history, is still found today in parts of the Pacific. Another type of animal with an equally long history is the sea urchin. I was engaged in prising out a fine specimen of fossil sea urchin from the Chalk cliff at Alum Bay, when I glanced down and there was a live specimen of the same animal on the edge of the sea. This was food for thought. What was the secret of its success? The answer is not far to seek for, living a simple life on the bottom of the sea, protected by a hard shell and spines, it had little to fear from its enemies. It should be good for several million years yet.

Following the uplift of the Chalk, there was a gap in the fossil record as far as the Island is concerned of about 5 million years, until the resumption of deposition of more sedimentary rocks, once again under estuarine, semi-tropical conditions during the Palaeogene period. Elsewhere, in the meantime, it would seem that rapid evolution had been taking place, for the plants and animals of this period were quite different from those encountered in the Cretaceous rocks, and were much more like those of today. Although mammal-like animals had been in existence since Jurassic times, they had been insignificant, but now they were to be dominant on land. Insects, too, had had a long history, but now they were to be found in enormous numbers and great variety. All the major groups of plants and animals developed during the Palaeogene Period, which makes it of particular interest. Locally there were frequent changes from fresh water to marine conditions and back again, giving an even greater variety of fossils, while the shallow estuarine conditions ensured that fossils of land-dwelling plants and animals are well represented.Modern methods of research have made great advances in recent years and over 80 species of mammals have been recovered by painstakingly retrieving their sometimes minute teeth by sieving through vast amounts of Palaeogene deposits. In spite of a long history of research, there are many fossils still to be found and the amateur collector has a valuable contribution to make, so long as proper contact is maintained and finds are made available to the local museum or other appropriate institution.

Following the period of uplift, the newly formed contours determined the pattern of drainage for the area, resulting in the Solent River system, which became established during the Neogene and Quaternary. The river followed the course of the present Solent, flowing eastwards, and was fed by tributaries, which still exist as independent rivers such as the Avon, Stour, Itchen and Meon on the mainland, and the three main rivers on the Island, the Western and Eastern Yar and the River Medina. At times of low sea level in the Quaternary, the Solent River flowed south and joined with various French rivers before flowing westwards down what is now the English Channel. The land to the south would have been continuous and joined to the Continent, so that during the Ice Age in the warmer interglacial periods animals and plants were able to migrate northwards and colonise the land. Remains of Straight-tusked Elephant, *Elephas antiquus*, and Hippopotamus, perhaps 70,000 to 120,000 years old, together with Bison, *Bison priscus*, have been recorded off the northern coast of the Island, which at this time would have been the marshy edge of the old Solent River. It was my privilege to make these discoveries, when camping with senior pupils of Island schools during the 1960's and 1970's. The students themselves were most adept at finding the specimens, which were then carefully

(Top) Clare Knight, with spade, and helpers prior to excavating the knobbly rock in the foreground, which Clare declared to be "bone". How right she was, for, when it was turned the right way up *(bottom)* it was a fine skull of a Bison, about 100,000 years old, and the almost complete skeleton of the animal was retrieved from the mud below, on the shores of the Solent.

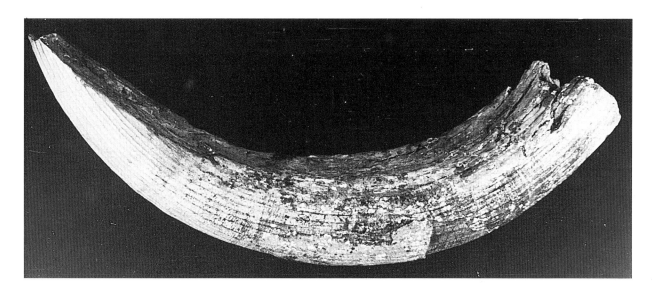

Tooth of *Hippopotamus* Sp. retrieved from the shores of the Solent in the 1960s.

retrieved between tides and soaked in rainwater to get rid of the salt, before being treated under the expert supervision of Cyril Lucas and later Dr Allan Insole.

Another interesting feature can be seen in the cliff at Brook. About six feet down from the top of the cliff there is a bed of gravel in which there is a dark band of peaty material. On inspection this proves to consist of large numbers of hazel-nuts, acorns and alder cones, together with leaves, twigs and branches of various sizes. These must have been deposited on the banks of the upper reaches of the Western Yar, some 7000 years ago, when there was still a considerable area of land to the south, which has since been eroded by the sea. local people aptly refer to them as 'Noah's Nuts'. They are not fossilised, but perfectly preserved, even to the extent of having discernible tooth-marks made by rodents.

It has only been possible to touch on some aspects of the geology of the Isle of Wight in a book of this nature, but it is hoped that this is sufficient to indicate what a fascinating subject it is. If you want to know more, you cannot do better than obtain a copy of the Geologist's Association Guide No. 25 – The Isle of Wight, by Brian Daley and Allan Insole, and follow the itineraries suggested in the text. There is also a useful list of references for further reading.

Million years ago	PERIOD			Stratigraphical Nomenclature in common use	
30	PALAEOGENE (Tertiary)	Oligocene	SOLENT GROUP	Bouldnor Formation	Hamstead Beds
					Bembridge Marls
				Bembridge Limestone	
				Headon Hill Formation	Osborne Beds
					Headon Beds
		Eocene		"Alum Bay Sands"	Barton Sand
					Barton Clay
					Bracklesham Group
					Bagshot Sand
			THAMES GROUP	London Clay	
				Oldhaven Formation	
60				Reading Clay	
65	CRETACEOUS			Chalk	
				Upper Greensand	
				Gault	
			LOWER GREENSAND GROUP	Carstone	
				Sandrock	
				Ferruginous Sands	
				Atherfield Clay	
			WEALDEN GROUP	Vectis Formation	
120				Wessex Formation	

Table to show the Stratigraphical Sequence in the Isle of Wight.

TWO

Flowering Plants

The flowering plants, which include our trees, shrubs, grasses, sedges and rushes, are the most immediately visible and accessible features of our countryside. Their study has its appeal at many levels. For some it is the sheer joy of seeing flowers like the Red Campion and Cow Parsley by the roadside, rather than the closely mown verges so frequently encountered. What can be more satisfying than a carpet of Bluebells in a wood, or the golden glory of Gorse in bloom? All one's senses are brought into play, as one hears the popping of the gorse pods on a hot summer's day, or one catches the lovely scent of Honeysuckle before one finds it hiding shyly in the hedge, or feels the velvety leaves of Marshmallow, quite the softest leaves in nature. How glorious the smell of pine needles, with the soughing of the wind in the tops of the trees, in a cathedral of pines, such as at Firestone Copse. What better than the taste of freshly-picked blackberries in the late summer, or the evocative smell of Water Mint crushed underfoot, as one skirts the marsh at Alverstone? All these can be enjoyed without knowing the name of a single plant, but most of us want to be able to put a name to what we see and know more about it, where it came from, how it lives and why it grows here and not there. The more one finds out the more interesting it becomes.

There are few places for which the occurrence and distribution of flowering plants have been so well recorded as in the Isle of Wight. It started with the publication in 1823 of *Flora Vectiana* by W. D. Snooke, which was not a full list, but an 'arrangement of the more rare and interesting plants indigenous to the Isle of Wight.' In 1836, however, a very personable young man by the name of Dr William Bromfield, of independent means and an outstanding botanist, came to live

Honeysuckle, *Lonicera periclymenum*, scents the air where it grows.

Primrose, *Primula vulgaris* - always a joy to see.

with his sister at Ryde. He soon made contact with Mr Snooke and other local botanists, including Dr Bell Salter, also of Ryde, and embarked on the task of gathering material for a comprehensive flora of the Isle of Wight.

This was not to be just a catalogue of plants, but each entry was to be accompanied by a detailed description based on his own personal observations and also the precise locations in the two halves of the Island, which he called the East and West Medina, where each plant was to be found. By 1850 he had made such good progress that he proposed to extend the scope of his flora to include the whole of Hampshire. This was not to be, however, for, with an insatiable love of travelling, he embarked on an extended tour of the Middle East and, in Damascus the following year, he contracted typhoid fever and died at the early age of 50. Fortunately, his sister committed the manuscript to Dr Bell Salter, who, together with Sir William Hooker, of Kew, undertook to edit the work and make good such gaps as still remained in the manuscript, which was finally published in 1856 as the *Flora Vectensis*. Although long since out-of-print, it still remains as the definitive work on Island flora to this day.

Other botanists of distinction have also contributed to our knowledge over the years. A. G. More published a *Supplement to Flora Vectensis* in 1872 and provided comprehensive lists of flora and fauna for the many guide books to the Isle of Wight, which were being produced at this time. *Wildflowers of the Undercliff* by C. O'Brien and C. Parkinson appeared in 1881 and covered a much wider area than the title suggests, and three years later saw the production of the *Flora of Hampshire, including the Isle of Wight* by Frederick Townsend, a scholarly work, but in which the Island records tended to be swamped by the numerous Hampshire records. A useful list, with short notes, bringing records up-to-date, by F. Stratton, was published in Morey's *Guide to the Natural History of the Isle of Wight* (1909), and thereafter numerous botanical records appeared in the annual *Proceedings of the Isle of Wight Natural History and Archaeological Society*, while J. F. Rayner published a *Supplement to Townsend's Flora of Hampshire, including the Isle of Wight*

Botanist extraordinary, Dr. W. A. Bromfield.

All-round naturalist, A. G. More.

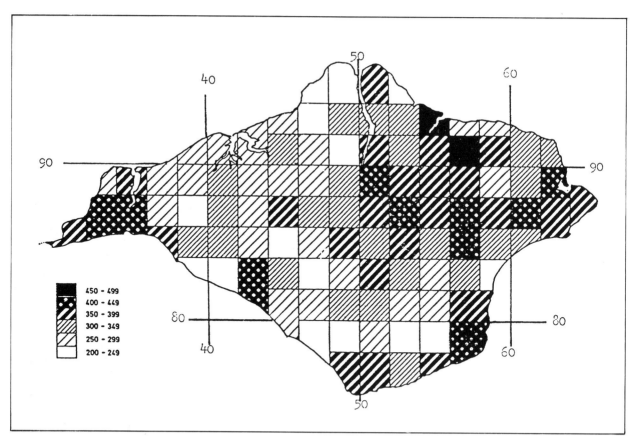

Map of the modified tetrad scheme used in the *Flora of the Isle of Wight*, showing the number of plant species recorded per tetrad.

in1929. Finally, all these records were collated and supplemented by a new intensive survey carried out by many botanists, both amateur and professional, resulting in the publication in 1978 of the *Flora of the Isle of Wight* by J. Bevis, R. Kettell and B. Shepard, which is an indispensable volume for anyone botanising in the Island. Mr Bevis unfortunately did not live to see the results of all his labours, but Mr Shepard, as Botanical Recorder for the Isle of Wight for the Botanical Society of the British Isles, maintains the records and added a short *Supplement to the Flora* in 1984.

So much for the documentation, but what does it tell us about the plants? Dr Bromfield tells us that on August 29, 1843, he discovered a species new to Britain. This was the Wood Calamint, *Calamintha sylvatica*, which your flora will tell you still grows 'on a single shady bank on chalk in the Isle of Wight', and nowhere

else in Britain. This should be a matter of considerable pride and joy, but, in reality, it is more of an embarrassment as, for obvious reasons, we cannot disclose the site where it grows, so that visitors are not likely to see it. In addition we have recorded a further 31 Red Data Book species, of which 16 have not been recorded recently, and 78 Nationally Scarce species, of which 11 have apparently become extinct. While excluding these on the grounds of rarity, this still leaves us with nearly a thousand species to enjoy, so there is no shortage of subjects for our attention.

The flowering plants, or *Spermatophyta* (seed-producing plants), form the highest division of the plant Kingdom and include most of our familiar and conspicuous plants. The plant body is differentiated into roots for taking in water containing dissolved salts, stem for passing water from roots to leaves and food to all parts of the plant, and leaves where food is made from minerals, particularly carbon dioxide and water, in the form of starch and sugar, using the energy of sunlight in the presence of green chlorophyll. A few plants, lacking chlorophyll, are unable to make their own food and so must be parasitic on other plants.

With the exception of the Gymnosperms, consisting of pines, larches, juniper and yew, which have naked ovules, all other flowering plants are capable of bearing flowers, of which the various parts are shown in the accompanying diagram. Many flowers are hermaphrodite, containing both female carpels and male stamens as shown, but other flowers may be of one sex only, and sometimes occurring on separate plants. Many flowering plants, however, such as grasses and sedges, as well as catkin-bearing trees, have no need for showy petals or sepals, because they are pollinated by wind.

Although, as we have seen, pine trees existed at the time of the Wealden, some 120 million years ago, most of our flowering plants evolved, together with the insects, the main pollinators, during the Palaeogene period and are now at the pinnacle of their evolution. Those plants depending on specialised vectors for carrying the pollen from one flower to another have a wide range of coloured petals, guide lines, scent and nectaries providing a sugary reward to entice the pollinators. Undoubtedly, the parallel evolution of flowering plants and insects, which are so dependent on one another, is one of the marvels of natural history.

There is no doubt that of all the wild plants to be found in the Island, those that bring most pleasure and interest to botanists, both amateur and professional alike, are the orchids, of which we have records of 27 species, which is more than half the total of those found in Britain. The reason for their popularity is no doubt due in part to the exotic beauty and glamour associated with the many tree-dwelling tropical orchids, but our own more down-to-earth terrestrial species still have the same attractive qualities of their tropical relatives, such as rarity, fragrance, delicate form and colour, together with in some cases fantastic resemblances to other forms of life.

A few of our orchids are tolerably common, such as the Common Spotted-orchid, *Dactylorchis*

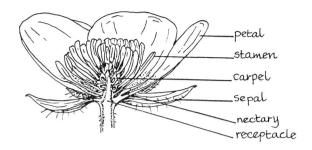

Diagram of typical Buttercup flower.

Ivy Broomrape, *Orobanche hederae*, lacks chlorophyll and is a parasite on Ivy, *Hedera helix*.

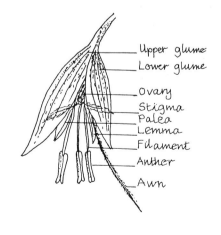

Diagram of typical grass flower.

23

fuchsii, found in a variety of habitats from woods to chalk downs. The Early-purple Orchid, *Orchis mascula*, is also common in woods, thickets and meadows, where it is often quite difficult to tell from the Green-winged Orchid, *Orchis morio*, unless one looks closely for the green stripes on the lateral sepal, in the latter. Both the Bee Orchid, *Orphrys apifera*, and the Pyramidal Orchid *Anacamptis pyramidalis*, although reduced in numbers from previous years, still persist on our chalk downs, although subject to annual fluctuations. Of the remainder most are extremely rare and only put in an appearance in occasional years. One of these was an Island speciality and for a time was actually known as the Isle of Wight Helleborine, *Epipactis vectensis*, until it was found to agree with a specimen which had been named a hundred years before as the Green-flowered Helleborine, *E. phyllanthes*. It was first recorded in 1917 and again in 1930 and 1954, but has not been seen since. This is an extreme case, but many of our orchids show a similar irregularity in flowering. The reason for this is explained by the remarkable life history.

Green-winged Orchid, *Orchis morio*.

Greater Butterfly-orchid, *Platanthera chlorantha*.

Autumn Lady's-tresses, *Spiranthes spiralis*.

Most plants have seeds with a store of food sufficient to enable the seed to germinate and grow into a new plant with green leaves fairly rapidly. The orchid, however, has such small seeds that there is no room for a food supply and germination depends on the seed having an association with a particular kind of soil fungus. This is able to derive nourishment from the humus in the soil, which it passes to the orchid by means of a 'mycorhiza' or fungus-root. In this way the orchid seed is able to survive and in due course put up some small green leaves of its own to make food for itself. It grows in size year by year, until it is eventually large enough to flower and once again produce more seeds. This whole process may take as long as 15 years to complete and naturally depends on the plant not being unduly disturbed during that time. In the past, unfortunately, people have thoughtlessly picked orchids and each subsequent year have noticed plenty more and not realised what damage they were doing. This may not be evident for up to 15 years later. Now we know better there is no excuse. It is vitally important that orchids should never be picked under any circumstances. A photograph or painting is a much more satisfying record than a shrivelled specimen could ever be, and there is the added satisfaction of knowing that the plant has been left to form seed, which in due course will lead to more orchids to delight future generations.

Comparing the plants of Bromfield's time with those we have today, we notice the changes that have taken place. There have been losses, as one might expect, but on the other hand there have also been gains. The main losses have been those of the cornfield weeds, due no doubt to the changes in agricultural practices, particularly that of re-seeding immediately after harvest, allowing no time for the weeds to develop their seeds, not to mention the more recent use of effective herbicides. The main casualties have been the lovely Cornflower, *Centaurea cyanus*, the handsome Corncockle, *Agrostemma githago*, the Pheasant's-eye, *Adonis annua*, the Wild pansy, *Viola tricolor*, and others, all of which were common and some 'far too common' according to Bromfield. Not everyone was sorry to see the

Frog Orchid, *Coeloglossum viride*, showing flowers with lips shaped like leaping frogs, giving it its name.

demise of these weeds. Farmers, in particular, were glad to be rid of Corncockle, whose seeds contained a poison that tainted the flour. What is surprising is the number of weed species which managed to survive.

On the other side of the coin, many plants have been introduced sometimes accidentally and sometimes by design, originating in gardens and then escaping into the wild. A good example of the former is the Pineappleweed, *Matricaria matricarioides*, which is like a small mayweed, but without petals, and with a strong smell of pineapple when crushed. It was first recorded in Britain in 1871, having been introduced with corn seed, and came to the Island by 1909, when it had a restricted distribution by the quay at Newport and by mills and farms in the centre of the Island. Now it is abundant in gateways and along farm tracks, even on waste ground in towns throughout the Island. It does no harm. Another plant, Oxford Ragwort, *Senecio squalidus*, so called because it escaped from the Botanic Garden at Oxford in the late 18th century, remained confined to Oxford until the seeds were carried along the mainland rail system, reaching Southampton and Portsmouth by 1940, where it was abundant on bombed sites. It didn't reach the Island until 1961, by which time its spread has not been so striking, but it is found on walls and on waste ground mainly in the East Wight.

Undoubtedly the most interesting gain is connected with the Cord-grass, *Spartina sp.*, which is a familiar sight on tidal mud on the northern shores of the Island. In Bromfield's time there was only a rather feeble native Small Cord-grass *S. maritima*, which he described as 'a rank-smelling grass, quite destitute of beauty'. Travellers to the Island at that time from Lymington would have passed between horrible-looking and malodorous banks of bare half-liquid mud, only sparsely colonised by the native Cord-grass. Bromfield does mention another American Cord-grass, *S. alterniflora*, which he had discovered in Southampton Water in 1836, growing with the native species, but he was not to know how important this was to be. In

You have to go out at night with a torch to see the Night-flowering Catchfly, *Silene noctiflora*, in flower.

Carpet of Ramsons (wild garlic), *Allium ursinum*, in a wood.

1870 James Groves and his brother reported the finding of a third kind of cord-grass in Southampton Water, which turned out to be a cross between the two species already mentioned. This was named Townsend's Cord-grass, *S. X. townsendii*, after the distiguished botanist, author of the *Flora of Hampshire, including the Isle of Wight*. This was a much more substantial plant and, with characteristic hybrid vigour, it spread with great rapidity and colonised the mudbanks in the Solent to the exclusion of the native species, spreading east-wards to Kent and Westwards to Poole Harbour. This was not the end of the story, however, for, in 1892, yet another Cord-grass was found in the Lymington River with fertile seeds, which must have arisen by Townsend's Cord-grass doubling its chromosome number and so creating a new species to be called the Common Cord-grass, *Spartina anglica*, which is now the dominant species throughout the Solent area. In the words of James Groves, 'we have here a natural hybrid produced probably within the memory of living man, through the accidental contact of a European and an American species, becoming permanent and forming a distinct 'species' more vigorous than either of its parents, and, like an unnatural child, doing its best at any rate on the Island to stifle one of them, but calculated to be of immense service to many by reclaiming much useless land and by preventing coast erosion'. It can be easily seen at Newtown, but there is evidence in some places that it is losing its vigour and dying off, so the story is not finished yet.

Flower spike of Common Cord-grass.

THREE

Non-Flowering Plants

For most people their knowledge of botany begins and ends with the flowering plants, which is a pity, as there is a new world of absorbing interest waiting to be discovered in the non-flowering plants. With the absence of flowers one has, of course, to look critically at other features in order to identify species, but with the aid of one of several good books one soon gets to know what to look for, and most species can be determined with the aid of a X10 magnifying lens, although for small specimens and some difficult species the use of a microscope is necessary.

The non-flowering plants may be considered as belonging to three main divisions:

THALLOPHYTA (Algae, Bacteria, Fungi and Lichens). This is the lowest main division of the Plant Kingdom, because the plant body, or thallus, is not differentiated into leaf, stem and root, as in the higher plants.

As one goes about the Island in high summer, one often sees a pond or puddle where the water has gone green. This is due to the presence of numerous single-celled (unicellular) plants of different kinds, two of which are shown in the accompanying drawings. They may be seen quite clearly under a microscope, but a colonial form of algae, known as *Volvox globator*, in which the cells are arranged in the form of a hollow globe, with daughter colonies within, can be seen with the naked eye, as it may measure a millimetre in diameter. The simplest multicellular algae (made of many cells) has the cells joined end to end to form numerous threads, commonly known as Blanket Weed. There are a number of species, including *Spirogyra*, with a spiral chloroplast. There is a simple form of sexual reproduction, known as conjugation, in

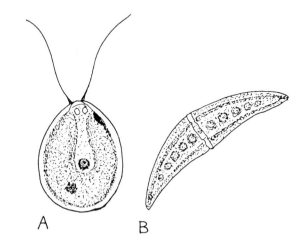

Single-celled *Algae*, (A) *Chlamydemonas* and (B) *Closterium* - a desmid.

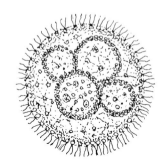

Colonial *Alga*, *Volvox globator*.

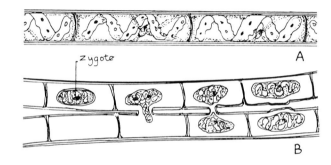

Diagram of *Spirogyra*, (A) filament and (B) in conjugation. For details see text.

which two threads lie side by side and grow out conjugation tubes to join opposite cells. The contents of opposite cells combine to form a zygospore, or resting cell, which is able to withstand being dried up and blown about as dust, before finding water again and growing into a new thread. All these algae are of vital importance being primary producers of food at the start of the food chain.

A more complicated alga is the Stonewort, *Chara sp.*, which grow, often in dense masses, in fresh or slightly brackish water, such as the pond by the shore at St Catherines Point. They are frequently encrusted with a chalky deposit, so that they feel gritty, and often emit a horrible smell. They have been much neglected, but in recent years a total of nine species have been recorded.

The Algae attain their greatest diversity and highest development in the sea, where they are known as Marine Algae or Seaweeds. These are divided into four main groups according to their colour, blue-green, green, brown and red. The Island shores are particularly rich in seaweeds, and some 284 species have been recently recorded (Farnham, 1982) and more have been recorded since. Bembridge is undoubtedly the best place for seaweeds and marine life in

Japanese Seaweed, *Sargassum muticum*, at Bembridge. Note how, when held aloft, the branches hang down 'like washing on a line'.

general, but other good areas are at Hanover Point and at Freshwater Bay, where one can make a direct comparison between the sheltered conditions on the west side and the exposed position on the east side.

The red algae, *Grateloupia filicina*, var. *luxurians*, and *Gracilaria bursa-pastoris*, of only local occurrence in the British isles, are found at Bembridge, while the brown algae, the lovely Peacock's Feather, *Padina pavonica*, and the Oarweed, *laminaria ochroleuca*, have their current eastern limits in the Island

As many shipping lines pass the Island, it is not surprising that a number of introduced species have been recorded. Chief amongst these is the Japanese Seaweed, *Sargassum muticum*, which was first recorded at Bembridge in 1973 and spread alarmingly both locally and along the coast as far as Plymouth. It has not proved to be such a nuisance as was at first thought, but it has colonised areas of mud to the positive benefit of other forms of life.

Bacteria and fungi do not contain chlorophyll and so must obtain their food by being parasitic on living animals and plants, or saprophytic on

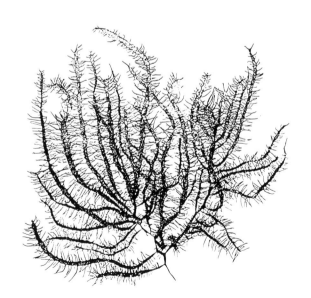
Grateloupia filicina var. *luxurians*.

dead ones. Some bacteria cause disease, but most are beneficial by breaking down dead matter into simple compounds which are thus made available to other plants. The so-called iron Bacteria are common in ditches and streams flowing through the lower greensand in the south of the Island, which is rich in iron compounds. They obtain their energy by oxidising the iron salts and precipitate iron oxide, making large quantities of rust-colour mud, characteristic of these areas.

Fungi, such as mushrooms and toadstools, are particularly well represented in the Island. An annual 'fungus foray' has been held for the last 35 years or so, and each year several species new to the Island have been recorded. The plant body of the fungus consists of a mass of threads, or *hyphae*, collectively known as the *mycelium*, interwoven with the food material. What we see and recognise as a fungus is, in reality, just the fruiting body, the purpose of which is to produce spores for reproduction. Fungi are divided into four main groups, according to how the spores are produced: (1) the *Phycomycetes*, or thread fungi, such as bread-mould, which produce spores in simple spore-producing organs or *sporangia*; (2) the *Ascomycetes*, which produce their ascospores, usually in eights, from flask-shaped *asci*; (3) the *Basidiomycetes*, which produce their basidiospores, usually in fours, on club-shaped *basidia*; and (4) the *Deuteromycetes*, in which spores are produced directly from the *mycelium*, as *conidia*.

The *Ascomycetes* are further divided into *Discomycetes*, with cup-shaped fruit-bodies, and *Pyrenomycetes*, with club-shaped fruit-bodies, from the surface of which ascospores are produced in great numbers.

The *Basidiomycetes* are further divided into the following groups: (a) *Gasteromycetes*, with the spores enclosed within the fruit-body until ripe, such as Stinkhorns, Puff-balls, Earthstars, etc. 33 species have been recorded, including the nationally rare Basket or Lattice-work Fungus, *Clathrus ruber*; (b) *Agaricales*, including the gilled fungi, such as the edible mushroom, and *boletus* species, with pores instead of gills. 592 species have been recorded, many of which are nationally rare and one, *Agaricus depauperatus*, new to Britain in

Peziza repanda, one of the elf cups.

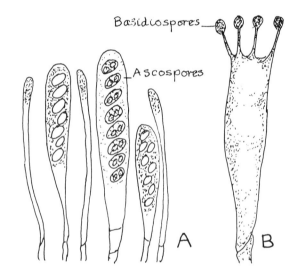

Diagrams of (A) an Ascus and (B) a Basidium. For details see text.

1988; (c) *Aphyllophorales*, including bracket fungi, coral fungi or fairy clubs, and the Hedgehog Fungus, *Hydnum* sp., with spines rather than tubes. 148 species have been recorded, including the nationally rare *Dendropolyporus umbellata*; (d) *Tremellales*, etc., the jelly fungi, of which 23 species have been recorded; and (e) Rusts and Smuts, which are important parasites on many plants, of which 55 species have been recorded.

The Deuteromycetes are a mixed lot of mould fungi, which include conidial stages of some higher fungi and small black microscopic flask fungi. Some 32 species have been recorded.

Puff-balls, *Lycoperdon perlatum*, which eject spores through the hole in the centre as the outer case contracts.

Earth-star, *Geastrum triplex*, like a Puff-ball with an outer case which splits and folds back.

Gymnopilus junonius, grows on dead tree-stumps.

Basket or Lattice-work fungus, *Clathrus ruber*, a rare kind of Stinkhorn.

Dryad's Saddle, *Polyporus squamosus*, one of many bracket fungi (photograph Clive Chatters).

Although not true fungi, the Slime-moulds, or *Myxomycetes*, may be conveniently considered here. Also called *Mycetozoa* (fungus animals), these interesting organisms have characteristics common to both animals and plants. They typically consist of a great number of swarm cells, which multiply by division and are highly mobile. They combine to form a *plasmodium*, in which stage it is aptly called a slime-mould. This breaks up to form fruits consisting of supporting structures and *sporangia*, which produce spores, which disperse and form swarm cells. So the cycle is repeated. 56 species have been recorded, but no doubt more will be found.

Lichens are dual plants, consisting of a fungus and unicellular algae living together for mutual benefit, in a state known as symbiosis. So close is this association that they are regarded as single organisms and named accordingly. The study of lichens is undoubtedly a most rewarding subject for the specialist, as they need special techniques for proper identification. Dr Colin Pope published a *Lichen Flora of the Isle of Wight* in 1985, which included details of 378 species, but a further 23 species have been recorded since that date, showing that a lot of work is still to be done with this fascinating group of plants.

There are three main types of lichens: (1) Fruticose, with the thallus erect and bushy or tassel-like, attached only at the base. Typical are *Usnea* sp. and *Ramalina* sp., usually on trees, and *Cladonia* sp., usually on the ground, but also on trunks and boulders; (2) Foliose, with the thallus growing out horizontally lightly attached to the substrate by means of threads called *rhizinae*. Typical are *Xanthoria* sp. and *Physcia* sp., growing on trees and buildings; (3) Crustose, with the thallus like a crust closely attached to the substrate from which it cannot be separated. Typical are *Caloplaca* sp. and *Leconora* sp., usually on rocks, but also on smooth-barked trees.

Lichens reproduce in two mains ways: 1 by the fungal partner producing spores. The resulting fungus will depend on picking up the necessary algal partner by chance; 2 by producing *Soredia*, which are microscopic granules consisting of a weft of fungal *hyphae* loosely enclosing a few algal cells, capable of growing into a new thallus, or larger *isidia*, which are outgrowths from the thallus, which break free and are readily dispersed. Both are equally important. Growth is extremely slow, so that lichens depend on a durable substrate on which to grow. They are very light-demanding and most sensitive to air pollution and over-enrichment by fertilisers, so that some species have been lost, though the Island's position enables it to share species with both a westerly and easterly distribution.

Old trees are major lichen habitats, and, although we have lost three species of *Lobaria* through air pollution, we still retain the magnificent Tree Lungwort, *Lobaria pulmonaria*, in two distinct sites. Churchyards are most important lichen habitats in the Island, where natural rock outcrops are rare or too easily eroded. Godshill churchyard is excellent, but some other churchyards have been ruined by tidying up and removing headstones. Old buildings like Carisbrooke Castle and the old Quarr Abbey are both valuable lichen sites.

BRYOPHYTA (Liverworts and Mosses). These were the first plants to live on dry land. They still require a film of water for part of their life cycle, so they cannot attain any great size.

Liverworts, or *Hepaticae*, are the simplest, consisting of a flat branching thallus attached to the substrate by elongated cells known as rhizoids. Some species, known as leafy liverworts, have leaves divided into segments, more or less flattened and in one plane, often with tiny scales or leaves beneath. They are confined to damp places, such as ditches, clay banks, by waterfalls and damp walls, and cannot withstand drought. Shanklin Chine is particularly good for liver-

Diagram showing structure of a typical foliose lichen.

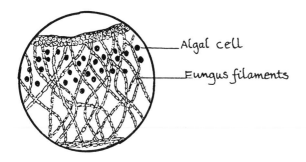

Algal cell

Fungus filaments

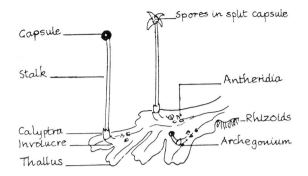

Diagram to show structure of a Liverwort.

A common Liverwort.

noted, there are two distinct generations, the thallus or leafy plant, which is the sexual generation, or *gametophyte*, and the stalk and capsule, which is the spore producing generation or *sporophyte*, which is parasitic on the *gametophyte*. This phenomenon, known as *alternation of generations*, is characteristic of bryophytes generally, as well as some of the higher seaweeds.

Of the 72 liverworts at present on the Island list, some have not been found since 1964, when the British Bryological Society held a field week here. This could be partly due to changes in agriculture and loss of acid areas, and partly because some are small and easily overlooked. *Blasia pusilla* has been flourishing on the base of the cliff at Shanklin at least since 1909, and *Southbya nigrella* is still in its only current United Kingdom site in the Island, since the Portland Bill site has not been confirmed in recent years. *Lophocolea fragrans* occurs in Cliff Copse, Shanklin, and *Marchantia polymorpha*, the type species of liverwort in text books, was a late arrival in the Island, but is now found in several places, having spread from garden centres.

Mosses, or *Musci*, are more highly developed than liverworts and are able to live in drier situations, although a film of water is still necessary for part of the life cycle, which is shown in the accompanying diagram. In many species

Diagrams to show life cycle of a Moss. (A) Sporophyte. (B) Gametophyte.

worts and well worth a visit. They reproduce in two ways: (1) by vegetative means, as almost any fragment of a liverwort is able to grow into a new thallus in the right conditions. In many species special buds, or *gemmae*, are formed and become detached to develop into new plants; (2) sexually, by the development of male and female organs on the thallus early in the year. A film of water is necessary, so that swimming cells produced by the male organ can swim to the female organ and fertilise the egg-cell, which grows into a stalk and capsule, which produces spores, which are dispersed and may, under suitable conditions grow into new thalli. In this life cycle, it will be

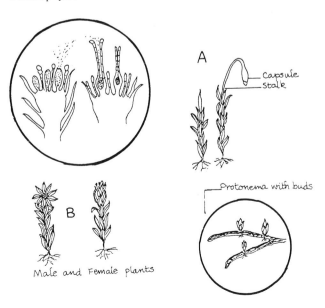

33

the capsule is a useful identification feature, and has an ingenious arrangement of teeth, forming the *peristome*, which open and close according to weather conditions and so allow the spores to escape when conditions are right for their dispersal. One of the peculiarity of mosses is their ability to withstand completely drying out. During the last war, when the Natural History Museum at South Kensington was bombed, some dried moss specimens, which had been kept in store for more than a hundred years, were soaked with water from the fire-hoses and immediately sprang into life and started to grow rapidly.

There are 272 mosses currently on the Island list, but again some have not been found recently. Farming practices have resulted in a decline in arable field species, while loss of acid areas, such as Bleak Down, has caused a decline in *Sphagnum* species, but they would return, if given half a chance. The recently rejuvenated pond at Parkhurst Forest, north of the car park, already contains four species.

To see a good variety of mosses at their best, one should visit a deciduous wood, such as parts of Parkhurst Forest, in March, before the leaves come out on the trees and block out the light. *Fissidens celticus* has been recorded from Parkhurst Forest. This is an Atlantic species very near the eastern limit of its range in this country. *Tortula* species are of particular interest. *T. papillosa* has recently been recorded from Niton on tarmac. *T. marginata* is quite common and *T. rhizophylla* (previously *T. vectensis*) is still in the ploughed field along the coast road at Brook. It was found in the Scilly Isles in 1984, but there are no other records for Great Britain. It seems to be a coastal or island species, judging by its world distribution. *Homolothecium sericium* is extremely common on walls and gravestones. *Funaria obtusa*, originally recorded in Parkhurst Forest in 1926, has been found there again in 1989, while *Mnium stellare* has been recorded in Bonchurch landslip since at least 1909, but nowhere else on the Island.

PTERIDOPHYTA (Ferns, horsetails and Clubmosses). This is the highest division of non-flowering plants. They are differentiated into

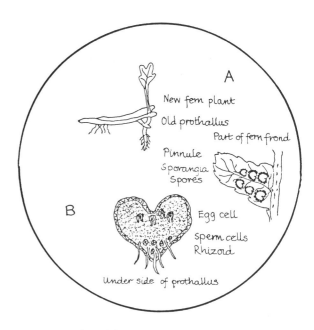

Diagrams to show life cycle of a fern. (A) Sporophyte. (B) Gametophyte.

Royal Fern, *Osmunda regalis*, with clusters of brown *sporangia* at the top.

root, stem and leaves, with a well developed vascular system, so that they qualify for inclusion with the flowering plants in the standard flora.

Ferns overcome the restrictions with regard to size and habitat imposed on liverworts and mosses by the simple process of making the leafy stage the sporophyte generation, not requiring a film of water, so that they can grow in much drier situations and be much larger in size. This is made possible also by the well developed root system and efficient vessels carrying food and water to all parts of the plant. Ferns still exhibit *alternation of generations* as shown in the accompanying diagram. Spores are produced from *sporangia* enclosed in *sori* on the backs or edges of the fronds according to species. The shape and arrangement of the sori are important identification features. Reproduction can also be by underground stems, or *rhizomes*, which spread out in all directions and send up new aerial shoots at intervals.

The common Bracken, *Pteridium aquilinum*, is a good example of this means of reproduction. 24 species of fern have been recorded in the Island, but five of these have not been seen recently. The Royal Fern, *Osmunda regalis*, and the Hard Fern, *Blechnum spicant*, have both declined owing to loss of acid habitat, but may still be seen at the base of the cliff at Lake and at Newchurch. The Sea Spleenwort, *Asplenium marinum*, is only found at St Catherine's Point, which is the south-east limit of this Atlantic species. Unaccountably a specimen appeared on the wall of the Roman Villa at Shide, near Newport, in 1969, growing very lushly, until it was removed in a clean-up operation. Rustyback, *Ceterach officinarum*, may best be seen on the wall surrounding Brading churchyard. The Marsh Fern, *Thelypteris palustris*, is a fenland species, which still grows in Freshwater Marsh and three other sites. The Water Fern, *Azolla filiculoides*, has been introduced and completely covers the surface of some ponds. The Adder's Tongue, *Ophioglossum vulgatum*, is plentiful in some years in some favourable sites, such as St Helens Duver and near the Longstone at Mottistone.

Horsetails belong to a group of plants which were dominant in Wealden times and before. They grew into large trees at that time, but the descendants are comparatively small. Reproduction seems to be largely by underground rhizomes. Fertile stems, without branches, are sent up by some species early in the year, bearing cone-shaped clusters of sporangia, which last for a time and then die down before the infertile stems with whorls of green branches appear. In other species the cones are produced on the green summer growths. The leaves are confined to small toothed sheaths at the joints of the stem, from the bases of which the whorls of green branches grow out. A section through the stem discloses an interesting arrangement of vessels of

Sea Spleenwort growing at Newport.

The Water Fern, *Azolla filiculoides*, grows on the surface of ponds.

Adder's Tongue Fern, *Ophioglossum vulgatum*, with spike of *sporangia*.

Infertile stems of Great Horsetail.

Fertile stems of Great Horsetail, *Equisetum telmateia*.

different sizes round the central hollow, which is characteristic of each species. These are necessary for a plant that grows in such wet situations. There are five species of horsetails in the Island, which shares the distinction with Ireland in having the Great Horsetail, *Equisetum telmateia*, in such abundance that it causes quite a conspicuous feature of the landscape. The much rarer Wood Horsetail, *Equisetum sylvaticum*, is found plentifully on farm land in Newchurch.

Although the Stag's-horn Clubmoss, *Lycopodium clavatum*, was recorded from St Boniface Down in 1860, neither this nor any other clubmoss has been recorded in the Island this century.

FOUR

Mammals

Much is made of the differences between our native mammals and those which have been introduced, but, if one thinks about it, all our mammals have come here since the end of the last Ice Age, about 10,000 years ago. Our native mammals, one presumes, are those that managed to arrive here before the land bridge from the south was breached by the formation of the Channel. The introduced species are those which have been helped on their way directly or indirectly by human agency. Undoubtedly some potential native mammals have, in fact, been introduced at a later date, so the distinction is not at all clear. We look to the geologist and the archaeologist for evidence of the early animals, which are most likely to be native.

Mention has already been made of the 'Noah's Nuts' at Brook, about 1,000 years old, with evidence of gnawing by rodents, but unfortunately it has not been possible to establish for certain the species involved. It would be well worth while to sieve this material and recover better evidence, such as teeth and bones. Hubert Poole (1934) recorded the tusk of a Wild Boar, *Sus scrofa*, in a cooking pot of Belgic type at Lake, but unfortunately a mass of bones had been shovelled over the cliff before he arrived. John Alexander (1964) in the excavation of a round barrow on Arreton Down recorded another large pig tooth, one canine tooth of Otter, *Lutra lutra*, fragments of antler of Red Deer, *Cervus elaphus*, and one mandible of *Felis* sp., possibly Wild Cat, *Felis sylvestris*. The whole assemblage was dated to Early Bronze Age, about 4,000 years ago.

In 1985 Dick Jones, of King's Lynn Museum, analysed the contents of 4th century barn owl pellets obtained from the buried remains of a Roman villa at Rock, near Brighstone. These were compared with the contents of present day pellets collected from a similar habitat at Newchurch and Arreton. The table of results makes interesting reading:

Species		Rock Roman Villa 4th Century		Present day Newchurch + Arreton	
		No	%	No.	%
Mole	*Talpa europaea*	1	0.2	0	0
Common Shrew	*Sorex araneus*	84	15.7	53	22
Pygmy Shrew	*Sorex minutus*	37	6.9	21	8.7
Natterer's Bat	*Myotis nattereri*	2	0.4	0	0
Barbastelle	*Barbastella barbastellus*	1	0.2	0	0
Bank Vole	*Clethrionomys glareolus*	8	1.5	34	14.1
Field Vole	*Microtus agrestis*	192	36.0	63	26.1
Water Vole	*Arvicola terrestris*	4	0.75	1	0.4
Wood Mouse	*Apodemus sylvaticus*	180	33.7	52	21.6
Harvest Mouse	*Micromys minutus*	7	1.3	0	0
House Mouse	*Mus domesticus/spretus*	1	0.2	3	1.3
Common Rat	*Rattus norvegicus*	0	0	6	2.5
Dormouse	*Muscardinus avellanarius*	17	3.2	8	3.3
TOTAL		534		241	

Of particular interest is the large number of Wood Mice, compared with the low number of Bank Voles in the 4th century sample. As we shall see, the Bank Vole does fluctuate in numbers considerably. The seven Harvest Mice are also noteworthy, as this species is very rare indeed today, largely through changes in agricultural practices. The absence of rats in the sample would seem to indicate that they had not yet arrived, although the black Ship Rat, *Rattus rattus*, is thought to have been introduced at around this time, but would probably have been confined to ships and warehouses in ports, where it is still most likely to be found. The Common Rat was a much later introduction. The single specimen of House Mouse is of special interest in that it does not agree with our present type specimen of this species, and may have been an early ancestor, but one cannot be sure on so small a sample. The records of two bat species are certainly the earliest records for bats in the Island. The absence of Water Shrew, *Neomys fodiens*, and the Yellow-necked Mouse, *Apodemus flavicollis*, is to be expected as neither are found on the Island today.

The most interesting records of sub-fossil mammalian remains were obtained by Dr Richard Preece (1986), who carried out an examination of landslip material in the Undercliff, where buried soils containing vertebrate and molluscan faunas were analysed. The most productive site was at Binnel Point, where identifiable mammal remains as shown in the following table were recorded:

VERTEBRATES FROM BINNEL POINT

	Lower soil (Unit C)	Upper soil (Unit E)
Cervus elaphus L., Red Deer	–	$LM_{1/2}$
Sorex minutus L., Pygmy Shrew	Left maxilla with P_4	–
Sciurus vulgaris L., Red Squirrel	Fragment of LI_1 (young)	–
Muscardinus avellanarius (L), Dormouse	Right mandible with fragment of I_1 and M_1	–
Clethrionomys glareolus (Shreber), Bank Vole	RM^1, LM^1, LM^3, molar fragment, right mandibular fragment	–
Microtus agrestis L., Field Vole	Right mandible with I_1, M_{1-2}, right M_1	–

Charcoal from the soil yielded a radiocarbon date of 4480 ± 100 before present (bp) (BM-1737). The presence of Red Squirrel and Dormouse is especially noteworthy, constituting the earliest and only secure British fossil records for these species. All the species, except Red Deer, are found in the Undercliff today.

There have been no records so far of White-toothed Shrews, *Crocidura* sp., Mountain Hare, *Lepus timidus*, Beaver, *Castor fiber*, Wolf, *Canis lupus*, Brown Bear, *Ursus arctos*, and Polecat, *Mustela putorius*.

Temporary escapes into the wild have occurred in a number of species, but there is no evidence of them having bred. A number of Red-necked Wallabies, *Macropus rufogriseus*, and Muntjac Deer, *Muntiacus reevesi*, escaped from Robin Hill Country Park in 1976. A Polecat-ferret, *Mustela furo*, was killed by a car at Newchurch in 1978. A Mink, *Mustela vison*, was captured in a boat at Shalfleet Quay in 1967, but escaped again and disappeared into a pile of rocks. This leaves some 37 species, which have been recorded as occurring in the Isle of Wight, as follows:

INSECTIVORES (Insect-eating). The hedgehog, *Erinaceus europaeus*, is the only British mammal with hairs adapted as spines, which are raised by special muscles in the skin. The spines do not cover the whole body, as the belly, tail, legs and face are covered with coarse hair. In very young hedgehogs the spines are white and soft, but become hard and coloured cream and brown as they grow older. There is no general moult as in most mammals, but the spines are lost and replaced at random throughout life. As can be seen on the distribution map, Hedgehogs are well distributed throughout the Island and plentiful in urban areas, where they are frequent visitors to gardens. They may travel long distances in search of food, which is very variable, consisting mostly of beetles and other insects, earthworms and slugs. Their droppings are distinctive, being long and thin, about 1cm in diameter, with glistening fragments of insects visible. They are mostly nocturnal, since their prey is more active by night, and they truly hibernate in a nest of leaves, reducing their body temperature to that of their surroundings. The ability to roll themselves into a ball completely covered with sharp spines is an adequate protection against natural predators, except the occasional fox and badger.

Hedgehog, *Erinaceus europaeus*, preparing to roll into a ball.

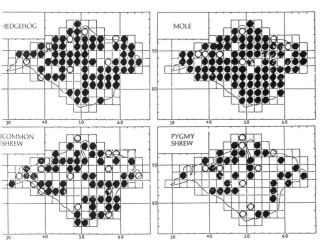

Distribution Maps of Insectivores in the Isle of Wight to January 1990.

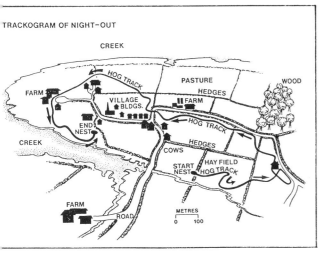

TRACKOGRAM OF NIGHT-OUT

A night's wanderings, based upon a male hedgehog that was followed all night at Newtown in his search for females and food (probably in that order of priority). He left his nest in a hedge, headed east to a garden, then across pastureland and through the village, finally going to bed at dawn in a small patch of weeds having covered more than 3 km (2 miles). (Drawing by Guy Troughton - reproduced from *The Hedgehog* in the Shire Natural History Series by kind permission of the author, Pat Morris).

It is not certain what effect slug pellets and other pesticides have on Hedgehogs, except that they naturally reduce the supply of their natural food.

The Mole, *Talpa europaea,* is not often seen as it spends most of its life within a system of tunnels beneath the soil, but its presence is evident by the molehills of excavated earth on the surface. The broad spade-like forelimbs attached

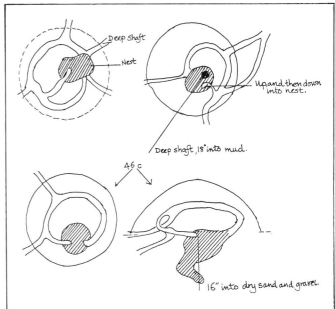

Drawings of Mole Fortresses by Lionel Adams in his Nature Diary (1901) (Redrawn by Dorothy Frazer).

to muscular shoulders are powerful digging organs. The pink snout is highly sensory, while the round tapering body is clothed in velvety silver-black fur, which hides the small eyes and ears. A lot of original research into the life of the Mole was carried out by Lionel Adams (1901), an outstanding naturalist, who was a member of the Isle of Wight Natural History and Archaeological Society. Details of the structure of a typical mole's 'fortress' were recorded in his personal nature diaries, which are in the possession of the Society's library. Food, which consists mostly of earthworms and insect larvae, is almost wholly obtained within the tunnel system, which acts as a trap. An adult mole requires up to 50mgs of food, or half its body weight per day to survive. It is active throughout the year, and fresh molehills can be seen forming dark patches above the snow. Colour variations have been recorded, including piebald specimens and a lovely shade of golden brown. In distribution the mole is ubiquitous and will probably be found in every kilometre square if searched for.

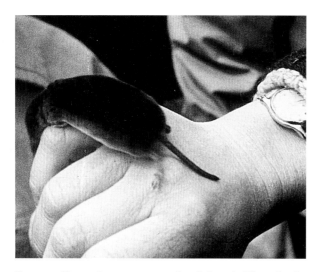

Common Shrew, *Sorex araneus*, with tail about half length of body.

mole. The Water Shrew, *Neomys fodiens*, was previously recorded as being common at Alverstone in water-cress beds, but it has not been recorded this century and in the absence of any further records must be regarded as extinct. The Common Shrew, *Sorex araneus*, and the Pygmy Shrew, *Sorex minutus*, are both found in the Island. The Common Shrew is the larger of the two with a tail which is about half the length of the head and body, dark brown above and paler below, while the Pygmy Shrew is much smaller, but with a proportionately longer tail, over two-thirds the length of the head and body, and is a paler brown colour. Lionel Adams also was the first person to point out that shrews were annual animals. The young of this year become the parents of the next year's generation and then die in the autumn. The Common Shrew feeds largely on earthworms, slugs, snails, spiders and beetles, while the Pygmy Shrew finds earthworms too big and concentrates on smaller items, such as spiders, beetles and woodlice. Both are widespread in the Island, but the Pygmy Shrew is generally not so common as the Common Shrew, except on saltmarshes, where the Pygmy Shrew will be the commoner species, probably due to the absence of earthworms. The young are retained in the nest until they are full grown, so there is no risk of mistaking a young Common Shrew for a Pygmy Shrew. When they first leave the nest, they may be seen 'caravanning', when each young shrew grasps the base of the tail of the one in front, so that the parent runs along with the young trailing in a line behind. It is certainly a wonderful sight.

CHIROPTERA (Hand-winged) Bats. It is not generally realised that there are more species of British bats than any other order of native land mammals. There are 15 species of bats in Britain, of which 10 species have been recorded in the Island since 1980, and a further two species previously recorded, but not confirmed recently. Bats are the only mammals capable of true flight, made possible by the flight membrane stretched between the elongated finger bones of the front limbs, the hind legs and the tail. All our bats are insectivorous and tend to be nocturnal as they feed on night-flying insects. They are able to detect their prey by emitting a series of sound impulses of very high frequency, beyond the range of the human ear, so that a detailed sound image of their surroundings is formed.

Bats are notoriously difficult to identify, even for specialists, so that records are mostly confined to dead or captured specimens, which have been examined closely and positively identified. Bats roost during the summer in hollow trees or buildings protected from direct sunlight, though females often segregate into large nursery roosts in a warm situation, and males roost in small groups nearby. Mating usually takes place in the

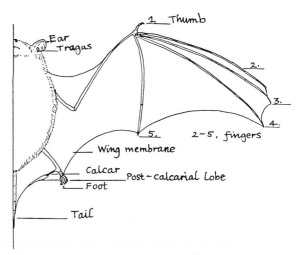

Diagram to show structure of Pipistrelle Bat.

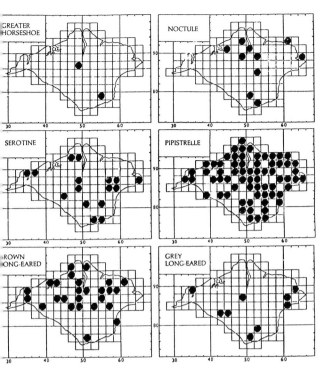

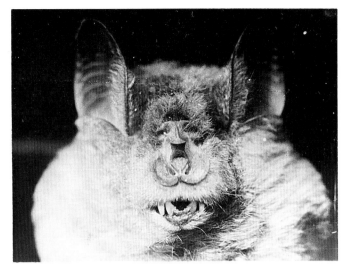

(Above) Face of Greater Horseshoe Bat, *Rhinolophus ferrumequinium*, showing the nose-leaf, from which it gets its name.

(Left) Distribution Maps of Bats in the Isle of Wight to January, 1990.

autumn, before hibernation, during which the female retains the sperm until ovulation and fertilisation occurs in the spring. Birth of young usually occurs in late June or July, during which the female turns head upwards, so that the single baby is delivered into a cradle formed by the tail membrane. The young develop rapidly and are able to fly within three weeks. In spite of this, bats are exceptionally long-lived animals, with a mean life-span of 4-5 years and maximum longevity of 20 years.

In the winter bats seek sheltered roost with a high humidity and steady low temperature. Hollow trees, caves, disused mines, tunnels, cellars and ice-houses may all be used for hibernation, when the body temperature is reduced to that of its surroundings.

The Greater Horseshoe Bat, *Rhinolophus ferrumequinum*, reaches its eastern limit in the Isle of Wight. It was much more common than it is today. It is distinguished by its large size and presence of nose-leaf. The Lesser Horseshoe Bat, *Rhinolopus hipposideros*, is similar to the last, but much smaller, with forearm less than 43mm. There are old records of this species, but its presence has not been confirmed since 1980.

The Noctule, *Nyctalus noctula*, is largely a tree-dwelling species and is almost certainly under-recorded. It is a large bat and distinguished from all others by its dark yellowish-brown fur, short ears and mushroom-shaped tragus. Leisler's Bat, *Nyctalus leisleri*, is similar, but of smaller size and with bicoloured dorsal fur. Although present on the mainland opposite, it has strangely never been recorded on the Island.

The Serotine, *Eptesicus serotinus*, is distinguished by its large size, dark brown colour, with bluntly pointed tragus and large white teeth. It is well represented on the Island, roosting in house roof spaces, especially in older houses, where they remain throughout the year. A striking silver-furred specimen was found in Carisbrooke Castle in 1986.

Pipistrelle, *Pipistrellus pipistrellus*, is the smallest, commonest and most widely distributed bat in the Island. It particularly favours modern houses with ill-fitting soffit boards under the eaves, so that it can gain access to the space between the soffit and the roof. It rarely enters roof spaces. Roosts of over 100 are quite common, and occasionally reach 200 or more. A single Pipistrelle will consume the equivalent of

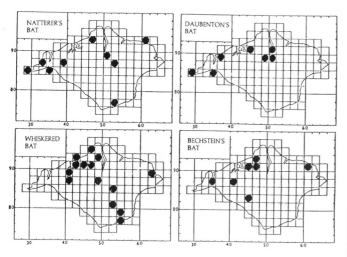

(Above) Distribution Maps of *Myotis* Bats in the Isle of Wight to January, 1990.

(Right) Grey Long-eared Bat, *Plecotus austriaca*, from Brighstone.

3,000 midges in one night.

Four *Myotis* species are present in the Island. Natterer's Bat, *Myotis nattereri*, and Daubenton's Bat, *M. daubentoni*, have a scattered distribution, mainly in the west Wight. They both utilise caves in the chalk near the Needles and at Freshwater for hibernation. Daubenton's Bats are particularly common at Newport and Carisbrooke. They are almost certainly under-recorded. The Whiskered Bat, *M. mysticanus*, roosts in houses in a similar way to pipistrelles, and is well distributed throughout the Island. They are slightly larger than pipistrelles and have a pointed tragus and longer fur. The similar Brandt's Bat, *M. brandti*, has not been recorded on the Island. The Bechstein's Bat, *M. bechsteini*, is one of Britain's rarest bats. There have been less than 200 records of this bat in Britain since records began, and 13 of these have come from the Isle of Wight. Of these no fewer than ten have been recorded since 1980. It is distinguished by its long separate ears, 20-26mm, not meeting above the top of the head. They are tree-dwelling and are hard to record, but they appear to be well distributed.

The Brown Long-eared Bat, *Plecotus auritus*, is the second commonest species, occupying roosts in house roof spaces and hibernating in hollow trees and caves. It is distinguished by its brown colour and enormous ears, which meet over the top of the head. The Grey Long-eared Bat, *Plecotus austriacus*, is one of the rarest of British bats and is well represented in the Island. It is distinguished by its grey colour, very black face and wider tragus. It cohabits with the Brown Long-eared Bat in a number of sites, and intermediate specimens between the two species are not uncommon.

The Barbastelle Bat, *Barbastella barbastellus*, was recorded at Carisbrooke in June, 1911, by H. G. Jeffrey, but has not been recorded again. It is another tree-dwelling species, which easily escapes detection.

LAGOMORPHA (Hare-shaped) Rabbits and Hares. It is known that the Rabbit, *Oryctolagus cuniculus*, was introduced into this country in the late 12th century. S. F. Hockey (1982) quotes documentary evidence to show that early introductions were

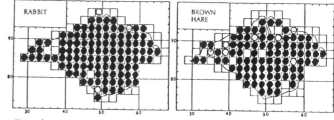

Distribution Maps of Lagomorphs in the Isle of Wight to January, 1990.

to islands, such as the Scilly Isles, Guernsey and Lundy. The first reference to the Isle of Wight was an account in 1225 of a well-established warren in the manor of Bowcombe, near Carisbrooke. Here among the expenses we find the wages of the keeper of 'conies', and among the receipts the sale of 200 rabbit skins. Although at first confined to walled enclosures, it seems they soon escaped and, in the absence of foxes, increased enormously until the arrival of myxomatosis in 1954 controlled their numbers. They seem to have interbred with domestic rabbits on occasions, as very attractive ginger specimens are often seen on Brading and Bembridge Marshes, while black specimens occur in a number of places, including Bembridge and Brighstone Down. The hare, *Lepus capensis*, distinguished by its long black-tipped ears, longer legs and a tendency to run rather than

The Red Squirrel, *Sciurus vulgaris*, is an Island speciality, as it has largely disappeared from southern England.

hop, is generally regarded as a native, but there is documentary evidence to show that their numbers were boosted occasionally by introductions (S. F. Hockey, 1982). Hares were not affected by myxomatosis, except that, as the rabbits declined, the hares increased in numbers and also in their range, so that today their distribution is about equal.

RODENTIA (Gnawing animals – Rodents). The Isle of Wight is almost the last stronghold of the native Red Squirrel, *Sciurus vulgaris*, in the south of England. It is widely distributed throughout the main woodland areas of the Island, and often comes to houses and raids bird tables. Distinguished by its usually rich chestnut colour with white underneath, pale specimens can still be told by their ear tufts. The large introduced Grey Squirrel, *Sciurus carolinensis*, which is common on the mainland opposite, occasionally comes over on the ferries, but has not become established here. Jessica Holm (1987) made a long-term study of Red Squirrels in the Isle of Wight, which makes most interesting reading.

The Voles have a rather long shaggy coat, blunt nose, small eyes and ears, short legs and

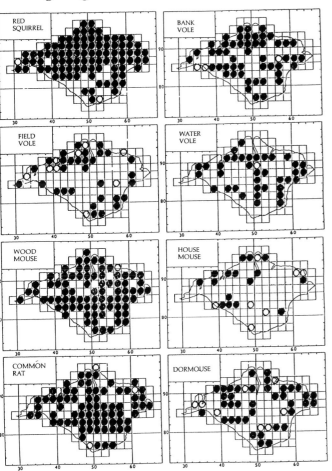

Distribution Maps of Rodents in the Isle of Wight to January, 1990.

43

Bank Voles, *Clethrionomys glareolus*, are remarkably tame.

Field Vole, *Microtus agrestis*, has a very short tail.

comparatively short tail, less than three-quarters of the length of head and body. They tend to be active by day. The Bank Vole, *Clethrionomys glareolus*, is the smallest with chestnut red upper surface grading into grey on the sides, with tail about half the length of head and body. It is widespread in the Island in almost any wood with a good ground cover such as ivy. The Field Vole, *Microtus agrestis*, is slightly larger, with a broader face, and of a greyer colour, with a very short tail. It favours open situations, such as permanent pastures and downland, but numbers fluctuate greatly. It is almost certainly under-recorded. The Water Vole, *Arvicola terrestris*, is the largest, being of rat size, but with a shorter tail and smaller ears. It is dark brown or almost black in colour and swims well. It is well distributed throughout the Island in suitable habitats, such as well vegetated banks of rivers, streams, ponds and drainage ditches.

Compared with Voles, Mice and Rats have

long tails, at least 80% of head and body, rather pointed muzzles, large rounded ears, sleek pelage and rather long hind legs and feet. The Wood Mouse, *Apodemus sylvaticus*, has dark brown dorsal pelage grading to yellow on the flanks. The ventral fur is pale grey and there may be a yellow chest spot. The tail is as long as the head and body. It tends to hop rather than run. It is widely distributed in suitable woodland habitats with sparse ground cover. It is strictly nocturnal. A long-term study of small woodland mammals carried out at Newtown from 1983 to 1986 (Frazer, 1988) demonstrated the differences between the annual fluctuations of Wood Mice, compared with the wider fluctuations of the Bank Voles, as shown in the accompanying diagram. The Yellow-necked Mouse, *Apodemus flavicollis*, is included here on the strength of only one recorded in a garden at Newport on February 17th, 1937 (Wadham, 1937). It has not been recorded before or since, and was undoubtedly an introduction. The Harvest Mouse, *Micromys minutus*, the smallest rodent, more like a vole in appearance, but with a long prehensile tail, is very rare indeed. It is included here on the evidence of a discarded nest being found at Niton in December, 1979 (Wilkinson, 1980). The House Mouse, *Mus musculus*, is supposed to have been introduced during the Iron Age, some 3000 years ago. It is of a dull greyish colour with a characteristic mousy smell. It is widely distributed on the Island, but is not nearly so common as it used to be. It can be numerous on some farms. The black Ship Rat, *Rattus rattus*, was recorded in the centre of Newport in 1942 (Wadham, 1943) and at Yarmouth in 1982 (Ford, 1983), and it is likely that it occurs elsewhere. The Common Rat, *Rattus norvegicus*, which was a later introduction, is widespread on the Island and probably under-recorded.

The Common Dormouse, *Muscardinus avellenarius*, is unusually common in the Isle of Wight. With upper parts of a uniform orange brown colour, underside paler with a pure white throat, the most distinctive feature is the hairy tail. It is strictly nocturnal and is the only British rodent to go into deep hibernation, usually in a closely plaited nest in the ground. They feed

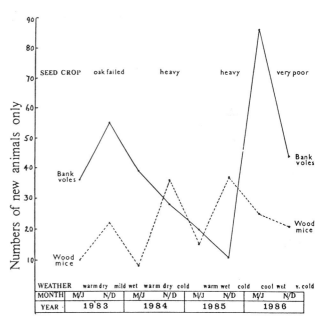

Diagram to show annual fluctuations in the populations of Wood Mice and Bank Voles at Walter's Copse, Newtown.

Common Dormouse, *Muscardinus avellenarius*, is common in the Island.

particularly on hazel nuts, which they open in a characteristic way, so that it is possible to tell the difference between nuts opened by wood mice, bank voles and dormice.

CARNIVORA (Flesh-eating) Fox, Weasels, etc., and Otter. The Fox, *Vulpes vulpes*, was introduced in numbers into the Island in 1845 for the purposes of hunting. A dog-like animal with erect black-backed ears, slender muzzle and long horizontally held bushy tail, it is widespread on the Island and particularly common in rough ground such as the Undercliff, where the hunt cannot exercise any control. It has recently become much more common in urban areas. An opportunist feeder, its main diet is of beetles and small mammals, augmented by fruits and berries in autumn.

The Pine Marten, *Martes martes*, was recorded in the Undercliff on a number of occasions in the early part of last century. In particular the Rev J. F. Dawson was enabled to approach to within a short distance of the animal and noted its distinctive orange bib. One cannot help wondering whether a Stoat, *Mustela erminea*, might have had its normally white throat stained by the Lower Greensand in this area, and possibly led to confusion. It has certainly not been recorded since. The Stoat is certainly not uncommon on the Island, and, in the severe winter of 1963, a specimen in the white 'ermine' coat was observed. One wonders how it knew at the time of the autumn moult that it was going to be so cold. The smaller Weasel, *Mustela nivalis*, is also widespread, but does not seem to be so common now as it was previously. The largest of this family, the Badger, *Meles meles*, has had a chequered career in the Island. It was probably introduced at about the same time as the fox, but it was deemed to have become extinct early this century (Wadham, 1909). It was re-introduced in 1925 to Lynn Common, near Newport, from which it spread and within ten years was established once again in its old haunts, mostly on the Lower Greensand south of the chalk. It does not build its setts on the chalk in the Island, which it probably finds too hard, due to compression. In recent years it has increased its range to include sandy deposits immediately north of the chalk and deposits of pleistocene gravels in the north of the Island.

The Otter, *Lutra lutra*, is rarely seen, but there have been recent sightings. It would seem that

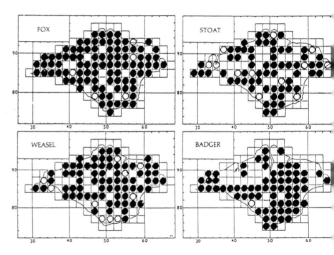

Distribution Maps of Carnivores in the Isle of Wight to January, 1990.

Stoat (top) and Weasel (below) compared for size and shape.

Otters on the mainland opposite occasionally swim across the Solent and enter our main rivers, where they may stay for a time. Unfortunately increasing development round the estuaries of these rivers and consequent pollution make this less likely to happen in the future, so the outlook is bleak.

ARTIODACTYLA (Even-toed ungulates) Wild Boar and Deer. We have seen how geological and archaeological evidence supports the view that Wild Boar, *Sus scrofa*, and Red Deer, *Cervus elephas*, were native species present some 5,000 years ago, but for long extinct. Worsley (1781) quotes documentary evidence to show that Red Deer and Fallow Deer, *Dama dama*, were hunted

Much-watched Badgers at Niton (photograph by Colin Fairweather).

in Parkhurst Forest and Borthwood in medieval times. It is likely, however, that both species were introduced for that purpose and became extinct early in the last century. The only deer on the Island today have been introduced to farms as domestic stock.

MARINE MAMMALS. These are divided into two distinct orders, which will be dealt with separately, as follows:

CETACEA (Whales, Dolphins and Porpoises). As these are wholly aquatic, there is some doubt as to whether they can be truly considered as Island mammals, but it is of interest to record those species which have had the misfortune to be stranded on our shores. Full details are given

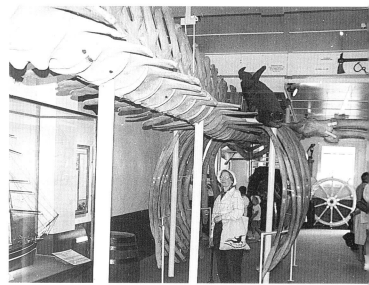

The skeleton of a Fin Whale stranded at Totland Bay in 1842 on display at Blackgang Chine. It is 80 ft. long.

Whaling in the Solent

Stranded off Bembridge

(Above) The Sei Whale, 40 feet long, captured at Seaview in
1888 (photograph, F. N. Broderick, Jun,. Ryde).

(Opposite) A page of illustrations by H. C. Seppings Wright,
which appeared in *The Illustrated London News* on 29th
September, 1888.

(Below) Fin Whale stranded at Atherfield on 16th May, 1924.
(from Lionel Adams' personal Nature Diary, Vol. IV).

by Frazer (1990), but the following is a brief summary of the strandings.

The earliest record of a whale being stranded was in 1758, when a dead whale was taken in tow by the *Alcide*, a man-of-war, which had to cut it adrift owing to a storm. It was washed up at a spot called Mackerel Rail, but ever since known as Whale Chine. Unfortunately, no-one at the time was able to identify it, but it was 63ft long. In 1798 a Bottle-nosed Whale, *Hyperoodon ampullatus*, 25ft. long, was captured in Southampton Water. In 1842 an enormous Fin Whale, *Balaenoptera physalus*, was stranded at Totland Bay. The skeleton can still be seen displayed at Blackgang Chine. Another specimen of this species was stranded at Atherfield in 1924, but this was only just over 47ft long. In 1843 the first British record of Risso's Dolphin, *Grampus griseus*, occurred when one was stranded at Puckaster Cove, and the body sent to the Natural History Museum at Kensington. Another one, over 11ft. long, was stranded at Shanklin in 1931. In 1888 a Sei Whale, *Balaenoptera borealis*, 40ft. long, collided with the ferry off Seaview and local fishermen captured the specimen and towed it ashore. This caused a great stir at the time and the artist, H. G. Seppings Wright, who happened to be in the Island at the time, recorded the event for the Illustrated London News. In 1853 a Pilot Whale, *Globicephala melaena*, over 15ft. long was stranded at St Lawrence, and two more of this

Bottle-nosed Dolphin stranded at Whale Chine on 15th June, 1963, at the moment of giving birth to a young one, which can be seen lying by the vent.

species were washed ashore at Bembridge and Brook in 1980. in 1936 six False Killer Whales, *Pseudorca crassidens*, were seen at close quarters by my cousin Deryk Frazer in Freshwater bay. During the whole period Common Porpoises, *Phocoena phocoena*, and Bottle-nosed Dolphins, *Tursiops truncatus*, were stranded at regular intervals, including one Bottle-nosed Dolphin which was stranded at Whale Chine in 1963 as it was giving birth to a young one. Since 1983 all five strandings have been of Common Dolphins, *Delphinus delphis*, and what is more worrying, there have hardly been any sightings or strandings of the Common Porpoise for the last 20 years.

PINNIPEDIA (Seals). Both Common Seal, *Phoca vitulina*, and Grey Seal, *Halichorus grypus*, occasionally visit our shores and haul out on to land for a time. The nearest colonies are in Cornwall to the west and East Anglia to the east, so they have come some distance. The Common Seal is most likely to be encountered in the sheltered waters of the Solent and north shore, while the Grey Seal may be seen off the south coast. Occasionally a dead specimen is washed up with injuries consistent with having been hit by a ship's propeller.

FIVE

Birds

With the wide variety of habitats in the Isle of Wight, there is clearly the potential for an equally wide variety of bird species, and this is supported by the experiences of local birdwatchers. In *Birdwatching in the Isle of Wight* by J. Cheverton and B. Shepard (1987), a most useful guide to anyone undertaking birdwatching in the Island, a Status List of Isle of Wight Birds recorded since 1950 comprises no fewer than 277 species, of which, however, 43 are rare and not likely to be seen again for some time. On a good day in a suitable habitat a competent birdwatcher can expect to record 50 species, increasing the total to more than 100 in a year and a possible 200 in a number of years. This would seem to compare favourably with most other areas of equivalent size in Britain, largely due to being a small island with a coastline providing a wide variety of coastal habitats.

Like the flowering plants, the birds of the Island have been well documented since the earliest list in Warner's *History of the Isle of Wight* (1795). From 1844 onwards for many years the Rev C. A. Bury, of Sandown, contributed regular observations and lists of Isle of Wight birds to *The Zoologist*, and was responsible for the list of birds in Adams' *History of the Isle of Wight* (1856). A. G. More built on this information, with the addition of his own records, in compiling lists of birds for Venables' *Guide to the Isle of Wight*, (1860) and many other popular guides produced at that time. Dr Meade-Waldo provided the bird lists for the *Victoria History of Hampshire and the Isle of Wight* (1900) and Kelsall and Munn published the most authoritative and up-to-date list in *Birds of Hampshire and the Isle of Wight* (1905). This again was used as the basis of the bird list by Reginald Fox in Morey's *Guide to the Natural History of the Isle of Wight* (1909). Reginald Fox, who incidentally was related to Charles Darwin, provided annual Bird Notes for the *Proceedings* of the Isle of Wight Natural History and Archaeological Society from 1923 until his death in 1933.

Thereafter there were intermittent notes on birds by Hubert Poole, Mrs Priestley and E. H. White, until a much more comprehensive Annual Bird Report was initiated by J. Stafford in 1953 and continued until 1983, after which, with a change of publication policy, a separate annual publication entitled *Isle of Wight Birds* appeared, in which the annual Bird Report is supplemented by other articles on birds, with original illustrations by Michael Webb. It is interesting to note that as time has gone by, with the growing numbers and competence of observers, the numbers of bird species recorded each year has increased from 153 in 1953 to 200 in 1963 and a record 227 in 1988. A further publication, *Breeding Birds of the Isle of Wight* by J. Cheverton (1989), which is a most valuable reference work for anyone studying Island birds, gives distribution maps of 126 breeding species, a selection of which is reproduced overleaf to illustrate points made in the text.

With this extensive documentation of birds of the Island, it is possible to see what changes have occurred over the years. It may come as some surprise to learn that losses have been extremely few, whereas there have been some surprising gains. The main losses have been the Red-backed Shrike, *Lanius collurio*, which used to be a regular breeding summer visitor, but is now rarely seen at all, and Sand Martins, *Riparia riparia*, which have decreased greatly in numbers over the last few years, largely due to disturbance at their

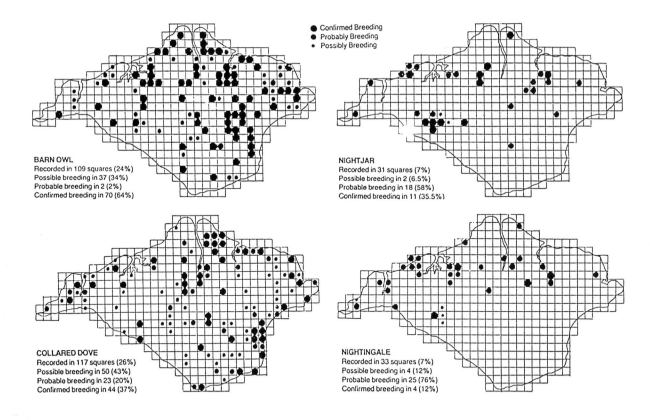

Selection of Distribution Maps for Breeding Birds in the Isle of Wight. (Reproduced from *Breeding Birds of the Isle of Wight* with the kind permission of the author, J. Cheverton).

few suitable nesting sites. The Puffin, *Fratercula arctica*, nested at Main Bench, Freshwater, until recent years, but is not thought to do so now, having withdrawn to Dorset. The Peregrines, *Falco peregrinus*, which bred regularly at Culver, Blackgang and Freshwater, and intermittently at other places, like other raptors, suffered severely from the effects of DDT and other chlorinated hydrocarbons in the food chain, and were completely absent during the 1960's and 1970's. Since then, however, they have been seen again in the breeding season at Main Bench, Freshwater, and there was evidence of their breeding there in 1987 and 1988. The only trouble is that their return to the Freshwater cliffs has resulted in the disappearance of the Kittiwakes, *Rissa tridactyla*, which had established a nice breeding colony there from 1969 to 1982, since when they have only been seen on passage. It seems you can't have everything. It is very much in the nature of birds, with their high mobility, to vary

in numbers from season to season, and year to year for a variety of reasons. One should not be unduly alarmed when numbers fluctuate. They will probably return. What is really important is to ensure that favourable habitats for a wide variety of species are provided and maintained.

The seabirds which nest at Freshwater and Culver Cliffs are of particular interest, as in most cases they are on the eastern edge of their breeding range. The main breeding areas are to the west and the ranges are dynamic, so that fluctuations in the numbers of birds on the periphery, as our birds are, reflect changes in the main population as a whole, which, unless gross, could not easily be detected by other means.

The Fulmar, *Fulmarus glacialis*, an oceanic species, visiting land only when breeding, was first noted prospecting the cliffs at Freshwater in 1953 and by 1973 was well established and in the next 15 years spread along the coast to Gore Cliff at Blackgang and Culver Cliff. It also spread

Black-headed Gull, *Larus ridibundus*, with chicks, at Newtown.

to Sussex and Kent, so it is clearly an extending species. The Cormorant, *Phalacrocorax carbo*, on the other hand, has been a long-standing resident, breeding at the Needles and Culver, and the range is apparently static. It has nested very rarely in Sussex and Kent, but otherwise does not nest between the Isle of Wight and Yorkshire. Much the same applies to the Shag, *Phalacrocorax aristotelis*, which also breeds in much smaller numbers on the Freshwater Cliffs and Culver, with no nesting between the Isle of Wight and Yorkshire. The Great Black-backed Gull, *Larus ichthyaetus*, is our largest resident gull and spread from Dorset to the Needles in the late 1940's, and has spread eastwards to Freshwater Bay and Culver. It even tried unsuccessfully to nest at Newtown, where it was mobbed by Black-headed Gulls, *Larus ridibundus*, in 1973. There is

no regular nesting between the Isle of Wight and Scotland.

Both the Guillemot, *Uria aalge*, and the Razorbill, *Alca torda*, used to breed in considerable numbers at Main Bench and Culver, but there has been a steady decline over the years, so that now there are only one or two hundred Guillemots and single figures for Razorbills at Freshwater and none of either species at Culver. Both species formerly nested in Sussex, but withdrew in the 19th century. Neither species now nest between the Isle of Wight and Yorkshire. The loss of the Puffin has already been mentioned. Apparently it never nested at Culver nor in Sussex, but it formerly nested in Kent, but withdrew in the 19th century. Now it does not nest between Dorset and Yorkshire. Opinions differ as to the cause of these declines, but one thing is certain, the oil menace takes a horrible toll. This is not

(Above) Herring Gull, *Larus argentatus,* has also taken to nesting at Newtown.

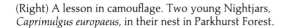

(Right) A lesson in camouflage. Two young Nightjars, *Caprimulgus europaeus,* in their nest in Parkhurst Forest.

new, for Reginald Fox drew attention to it in the 1920's and pleaded for something to be done. Here we are, in this enlightened age, still waiting. Accidents, of course, can and do happen, but a lot of the oil in the sea is put there deliberately and something could be done about it.

What is strange is that some woodland birds, which are common on the mainland opposite, have always been rare or absent from the Island. The Nuthatch, *Sitta europaea,* for instance, has occasionally been recorded from Osborne, and one was seen carrying food in 1955 at Niton. There have been two other occasions when breeding was indicated in suitable habitats, but no nest was found. Seeing how common it is in the New Forest, just a few miles away, it is a mystery why, in all this time, it has not become established on the Island. The Wood-lark, *Lullula arborea,* is another absentee, which is greatly missed as its call is so melodious. The Tawny Owl, *Strix aluco,* which is common on the mainland, although occasionally reported, is regarded as a scarce non-resident with no con-firmed records of breeding in the last 50 years or more. The Barn Owl, *Tyto alba,* on the other hand, is tolerably common and can often be seen quartering the fields at dusk. The breeding dis-tribution map shows its general range.

Some species have declined owing to loss of suitable habitat. A good example of this is the Nightingale, *Luscinia megarhynchus,* which was once an abundant summer visitor to the Island and found in every copse on the east side (Fox, 1909). In the last 50 years it has drastically declined almost certainly due to the cessation of traditional coppicing, which ensured a regular supply of woodland of the right height for the Nightingale. The distribution map shows where it has nested in the last 50 years, and recently it has diminished even more in the east Wight, so that it can be reliably heard only along the Western Yar, at Bouldnor and Clamerkin, near Newtown, where its preferred habitats of damp thickets or blackthorn scrub are available.

On the other hand, there have been some spectacular gains. Reginald Fox (1909) stated that he had never seen a Green Woodpecker, *Picus viridus,* in the Island, yet, after the Great War, in his Bird notes for 1925 he was able to state that they were common, and they have certainly been common ever since. The Great Spotted Wood-pecker, *Dendrocopos major,* was also scarce in 1909 and later increased in numbers. Reginald Fox, in his Bird Notes for 1932, was the first to record the Great Spotted Woodpecker visiting a bird table at Seaview, a habit which has since become commonplace not only in the Isle of Wight, but on the mainland also. The Nightjar, *Caprimulgus europaeus,* was much commoner 40 years ago. As the distribution map shows, breeding appears to be confined to open woodland in Brighstone Forest, Parkhurst Forest, Firestone Copse, Bouldnor and Mottistone.

In a National Census of Rookeries carried out in 1975, it was shown that the Island had the highest density of nests in the whole of Britain. The loss of all our mature elm trees in the 1970's due to Dutch Elm Disease forced many long-established rookeries to move to other trees, and the Great Storm of October 1987 caused further distress. They seem to have a great capacity for recovering from such disasters. Opinions differ as to the extent to which Rooks do more damage than good and should be regarded as pests, but extensive investigations have shown that on balance they do more good than harm. There is certainly no excuse for the not infrequent practice of shooting up rookeries, when the young are in the nest. This is a barbaric act that should be condemned by all right-thinking people. Fortunately Rooks seem able to maintain their numbers in spite of such treatment, showing that it is ineffective as well as brutal.

One of the most remarkable gains in recent years has been that of the Collared Dove, *Streptopelia decaocto*, which first arrived in the Island in 1962, having spread from Bulgaria and Turkey across Europe during the previous thirty years. Once it arrived, it spread most rapidly and is now a common resident breeding throughout the

The Kestrel, *Falco tinnunculus*, is still common on our downs (photograph, Barry Angell).

Island, as the distribution map well shows.

In common with Hampshire and Dorset, the Island has a few pairs of the Dartford Warbler, *Sylvia undata*, which, unlike most other warblers, is a resident staying for the winter, and nests in suitable habitats, where there is an abundance of gorse, particularly on the downs. It is surprising that it managed to survive the severe winter of 1962-3. This is a fully protected species and, if seen, no attempt should be made to find its nest or cause any disturbance whatsoever, without a licence from the Nature Conservancy Council (NCC).

Mention of the severe winter of 1962-3 reminds me of an occurrence which received considerable publicity at the time. It was in January, 1963, when the cold was most intense, that T. V. Pretty, of Noke Common, near Parkhurst, noticed that a nestbox on the side of the shed opposite the kitchen window was being used as a communal roost by numerous Wrens, *Troglodytes troglodytes*. The box measured only 125mm (5ins.) by 150mm (6ins.) by 175mm (7ins.) and was partially filled with nesting material. In spite of this the Wrens squeezed in one after another, so a careful count had to be made. On January 8th no fewer than 51 Wrens entered the box, which was an all time record and a film of this remarkable event was shown on BBC television.

In spite of this, however, the cold spell was so prolonged, lasting until March, that Wrens and other small birds such as the Coal Tit, *Parus ater*, and the Long-tailed Tit, *Aegithalos caudatus*, suffered severely from the winter and only few were to be seen at all for several years. Likewise, the Kingfisher, *Alcedo atthis*, suffered a severe decline, although it did seem to recover, so that there was usually a breeding pair along each river, until more recently when there has been another decline for reasons unknown. This, too, is a Schedule 1 species and is fully protected at all times, and no attempt should be made to approach or examine its nest without a Nature Conservancy licence. On the other hand, Blue Tits, *Parus caeruleus*, and Great Tits, *Parus major*, were virtually kept alive by the provision of food and water on bird tables, and the numbers of dead molluscs on the shore, which had been killed by the frost, provided ample food for the seabirds, which consequently benefitted.

Apart from the residential species the Island is well placed to receive many summer visitors, most of which breed with us. There is much more movement of birds than one might suppose. For instance, all Great Tits look much alike and one might well think that they are the same birds that come so regularly to the bird table. But a first winter Great Tit was ringed in Brighstone on 20th February 1960, and only three weeks later, on 14th March, the ring was returned from Holland, the bird having been killed by flying into glass at Wassenaar, near the Hague (J. Stafford, 1960). It seems likely that the bird had come to the Island in the autumn of 1959, and had, in fact, gone home. They certainly move about.

Talking of moving, the Island is exceptionally well placed for the observation of migrants, being on one of the main migration routes in both spring and autumn. To the dedicated birdwatcher the spring watch at dawn at St Catherine's Lighthouse is the high point of the birdwatcher's calendar. From March to May the passage is from west to east, and divers, gulls, terns and skuas may be seen in variety and large numbers. With experience, even at some distance, the species can be identified by its flight pattern. Auks may be seen flying low over the sea, while waders of many kinds may come close enough to be identified by sight. Many species of ducks will be seen and flocks of small landbirds will often be seen flying in from the sea and making their first landfall in the surrounding fields and bushes. It was at St Catherine's that the Royal Society for the Protection of Birds (RSPB) first put up perches round the lighthouse for the birds to perch on, and later illuminated the lighthouse itself so that the birds could see it. In the autumn, probably the best vantage point from which to see the movement of terns, skuas and gulls from east to west is at Fort Victoria, once again at dawn, as they come quite close. One must be prepared for discomfort and also for disappointment, and, for the beginner, it is essential that an experienced birdwatcher is present.

Robin, *Erithacus rubecula*, taking food to nestlings at Porchfield (photograph, Barry Angell).

Some birdwatchers like to work on their own, but one of the advantages of working in a group is that one can take part in various national surveys and so help to increase our knowledge of birds. In 1947 the Severn Wildfowl Trust (now the Wildfowl and Wetlands Trust) organised nation-wide Wildfowl Counts. Some 1000 volunteers undertook to count swans, geese and ducks on the middle Sunday of each month from September to March at about 1200 coastal and inland sites throughout the United Kingdom. In the 1950's a Birds of Estuaries Enquiry, run jointly by the British Trust for Ornithology (BTO), the NCC and the RSPB, was instituted to monitor all British estuaries by a series of synchronised monthly counts. The national results of both the Wildfowl Counts and the Birds of Estuaries Enquiry are published annually in *Wildfowl and Wader Counts*, and the local results in *Isle of Wight Birds*. Such data are invaluable in support of conservation cases when important wetlands are threatened.

In the 1960's with growing concern on the effects of oil on seabirds, the RSPB organised the Beached Birds Survey, involving the regular patrolling of the coast and recording numbers and species of birds found dead. Would that it was never necessary.

SIX

Reptiles, Amphibians and Fish

REPTILIA (Creeping animals). Reptiles are characterised by having skin clothed in scales and in being wholly air-breathing by means of lungs throughout their lives. Those with which we are concerned are divided into two main orders, and notes are given on some introduced or absent species.

SQUAMATA (scaled reptiles), which are divided into two sub-orders:

OPHIDIA (Snakes). The Ringed or Grass Snake, *Natrix natrix* is generally olive-green, tending to brown, with vertical black bars along its sides and two rows of smaller spots along its back. Its main distinguishing feature, however, is the yellow collar just behind the head, with a black border behind it. It is a slim and graceful snake, and may attain a length of 5ft, although specimens are usually up to three feet long. It is completely harmless, although, when adopting a defensive attitude, it hisses and pulls back as though to strike in quite an alarming manner. It is a good climber and also swims well. It usually feeds on frogs, occasionally taking toads, and is known to eat tadpoles and small fish. Like all snakes, they eat their prey whole, as their jaw-bones are connected by elastic ligaments. When freshly caught they tend to discharge a thick fluid from glands in the vent, which has a strong smell of garlic. They mate in April or May, and the female lays her eggs in some warm spot such as a compost heap. Each egg is oval and about an inch long, with a parchment-like skin. The batch of eggs is covered with a secretion, which dries and sticks them together. They usually hatch in August or September, and the young snakes are like small editions of their parents. They hibernate in holes or hollow trees, but are easily tempted out during a

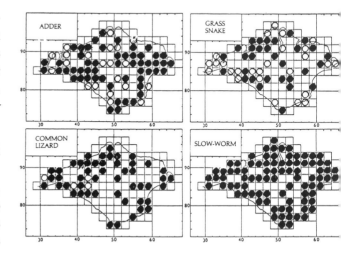

Distribution Maps of Reptiles in the Isle of Wight to January, 1990.

Grass or Ringed Snake. Note the yellow collar.

warm spell. From the distribution map it will be seen that they are widely distributed in the Island in favourable habitats, but there are indications that there has been a considerable reduction since the 1960's.

The Adder or Viper, *Vipera berus*, is variable in colour, but can readily be identified by the broad zig-zag stripe down the middle of its back. This is particularly clear in males, when the ground colour tends to be lighter. The reddish or pale specimens are usually females. Occasionally more or less wholly black adders are found, when the zig-zag stripe is hard to see, but the short thick body and stumpy tail are characteristic. It may grow to 30 inches in length, but is usually up to 18 inches. They have a poisonous bite, injecting the poison by means of two hinged fangs in the upper jaw. It is very seldom fatal, even in the case of dogs being bitten, and the adder is by nature a timid snake, and will always retreat if it can. It is ovo-viviparous, which means that the female retains the fertilised eggs in her body, until they are ready to hatch, usually in August, when the young are born alive. They resemble their parents. Hibernation is the same as in the Grass Snake, with which they are sometimes found. The Adder is also widespread and would seem to be commoner than the Grass Snake, but would also seem to have been reduced in numbers since the 1960's.

There has been no official record of the Smooth Snake, *Coronella austriaca*, in the Island, although it is found on the adjacent mainland.

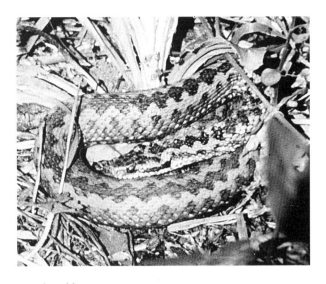

Female Adder.

Head of male Adder showing characteristic V marking.

Black Adder in Parkhurst Forest. Note the zigzag marking is barely visible, but the squat shape and short tail are distinctive.

(Above) Typical adult male Slow-worm. Note that it has lost the end of its tail.

(Below) Common Viviparous Lizard in characteristic pose.

SAURI (Lizards). The Slow-worm, *Anguis fragilis*, although snake-like in appearance is really a legless lizard. It has movable eyelids and is able to snap off its tail in the same way as other lizards. It is smooth, almost polished, and, in spite of its name, can move fast on occasions. It is absolutely harmless and will get tame. They are also ovoviviparous, the young hatching soon after the eggs are laid in August. All young Slow-worms have a yellow back, with a thin dark stripe down the centre and dark brown sides. Females tend to retain this pattern as adults and have a head which is small in proportion to its body. Adult males lose these markings and become a uniform shade of brown or grey, or occasionally other colours. Some adult males have bright blue spots, and this variety is especially well-known on the Island. They are well distributed throughout the Island and often seen in gardens, where they should be encouraged as their main food is slugs.

The Common Viviparous Lizard, *Lacerta vivipara*, varies in colour from light to dark brown, with variable markings. Males show quite a lot of green on occasions. The belly is pale orange. They are active and feed on insects, especially young grasshoppers. As their name implies, they are viviparous, meaning that they give birth to living young, which are almost black, in July and August. They are widely distributed, but almost certainly under-recorded, owing to the difficulty of encountering them as they hear one coming and scuttle away.

The Sand Lizard, *Lacerta agilis*, has not so far been officially recorded in the Island, although found on the mainland opposite. There is, however, a thriving colony of Wall Lizards, *Podarcus muralis*, which must have been introduced from the Continent some time ago, now well established on cliffs and in gardens at Ventnor. Males are a brilliant green and most attractively marked.

CHELONIA (Turtles, Terrapins and Tortoises). A young specimen of the Loggerhead Turtle, *Caretta caretta*, was found on the beach between Porchfield and Newtown in 1899 by Percy Wadham, and kept alive for a time (Wadham, 1909). It was unusual for this species to wander so far north from its usual base off the coast of Portugal, but with the warming up of the oceans it is likely that further specimens will be recorded.

In August, 1952, a specimen of the European Water Terrapin, *Emys orbicularis*, was found wandering on the beach at Chale. This species had been introduced to a pond at Old Park, St Lawrence, by Lord Walsingham in the last century. There were plenty still there in 1907 (Wadham, 1909) and probably for some time after that. After World War II, however, the pond was converted into a Tropical Bird Park, so it is just possible that this specimen was one of the last survivors.

Tortoises of various species were commonly sold as pets and no doubt many of these escaped. On three separate occasions I have come across tortoises wandering freely in my own garden at Brighstone. One wonders how many of them there are living wild and for how long they are likely to survive. Their eggs have been successfully hatched and the young reared in captivity, but it is unlikely that they could breed in the wild in our climate. Two species are usually involved – Hermann's Tortoise, *Testudo hermanni*, and the Spur-thighed Tortoise, *Testudo graeca*, both from Greece.

AMPHIBIA (Leading two lives) include the Frogs, Toads and Newts. They are characterised by having a naked skin, and having two distinct stages in the course of their development. The eggs, which are laid in water, hatch into larvae, which breathe by means of gills, until later on when lungs develop and they come out of the water to live on land, returning to the water to breed some time later. The following species are found on the Island:

ANURA (Without tails in the adult form – Frogs and Toads). The Common Frog, *Rana temporaria*, has smooth skin. The colour is variable, usually brownish, with variable darker spots and bands, and a dark brown temporal patch round the eardrum. The male can be distinguished by the dark pad on the thumb. Spawn is laid in clumps in shallow water. The tadpoles are olivaceous with tiny gold spots, and have a sharp point to the

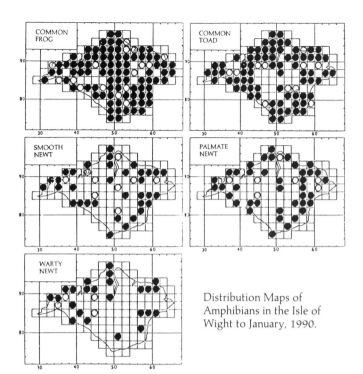

Distribution Maps of Amphibians in the Isle of Wight to January, 1990.

The Common Frog. Note the temporal patch, which is a constant feature (photograph, Barry Angell).

tail. Distribution is widespread, except on downland where there is a lack of ponds.

The Common Toad, *Bufo bufo*, has a drier warty skin. The colour is also variable from grey through brown to almost black. Brick-red specimens are not uncommon. Not so active as frogs, they tend to crawl rather than hop. They are easily tamed. The spawn is laid in strings, wound round water plants, in the deeper parts of communal ponds, to which many hundreds of toads may travel from a wide are in the spring. The tadpoles are almost black, and have the end of the tail bluntly rounded. Their distribution is also widespread, but the most interesting populations are on the slipped cliffs at Compton Bay and Whale Chine, where they must regularly be subjected to salt spray. The toads seem smaller than usual and very dark-skinned.

Common Toad (photograph, Barry Angell).

Spawn of the Common Toad. Note double row of eggs.

As observers had remarked that frogs seemed to have been getting scarcer in recent years, members of the Isle of Wight Natural History and Archaeological Society, assisted by pupils of Island schools, carried out a survey in 1964 to determine the Frog and Toad Spawning Areas, and compare them with records of previous years. The survey was repeated in 1966, 1968, 1970, 1975 and 1980. These were fully reported in the Proceedings of the Society for each of those years. The results showed that there had been a significant reduction in Frogs, probably due to filling in of ponds and the severe winter of 1963. Toads, however, had not seemed to have been so affected. Over the period of the surveys there was a steady recovery so far as the Frogs were concerned.

In addition to the above, there have been a number of introductions. The European Tree Frog, *Hyla arborea*, was introduced to a pond at St Lawrence in the latter part of last century, where it was still breeding in 1962, but fell victim to the severe winter of 1963. Efforts to re-introduce it to my own pond at Brighstone in 1978 and 1979 were unsuccessful. In 1967 Frank Boyce, of Freshwater, liberated a number of African Clawed Toads, *Xenopus laevis*, into a small pond on the cliffs at Brook. Tadpoles were found in the pond in 1970, and in 1974 a number were discovered in a pond nearby. In 1976 the population was estimated at between forty and fifty individuals, and they continue to thrive, in spite of the droughts in 1976 and 1989, when the ponds appeared to have dried up completely.

CAUDATA (Retaining tails throughout life – Newts). The Common Smooth Newt, *Triturus vulgaris*, is the least aquatic, leaving the water soon after breeding. The male only develops a continuous notched crest along the back and under the tail. It is boldly spotted. The female has small spots under the chin.

The Palmated Newt, *Triturus helvetica*, is the most aquatic, often found in ponds even in the winter. The male is distinctive with black webbed hind feet, and the end of the tail appears truncated, but continuing as a slender black filament. It has a slight crest, mostly above and below the tail. The female has no spots under the chin.

The Warty Newt, *Triturus cristatus*, is the largest newt, reaching six inches in length. The male develops a notched crest, interrupted at the base of the tail. Females are dark brown with tiny white warts, especially on the sides. Both sexes have bright orange bellies, variously spotted. Neotonous individuals sometimes occur, failing to change to the adult form, and so retaining their gills to a much larger size then usual.

A survey of newts was carried out in 1965, and records obtained since then have shown that the Palmate Newt is the most widespread and numerous, the Common Smooth Newt is equally widespread but not so numerous, while the Warty Newt is the rarest, but, where it occurs, is quite plentiful.

PISCES (Fishes) differ from the other classes of vertebrate animals in spending the whole of their lives in water, breathing by means of gills. Their skins are usually covered with scales, and their limbs are usually adapted as fins. They are divided into three sub-classes. In the following notes particular attention is paid to the fresh water fish found in the Island, but lists are given of those marine species, which have been recorded round our coasts. Numbers of species, where appropriate, are given in brackets:

ELASMOBRANCHII (Cartilaginous fishes). These are all marine, and include Shark (5), Spotted Dogfish (2), Smooth-hound, Tope, Monk-fish, Skate and Rays (7).

TELEOSTOMI (Bony fishes).

Perch Family. The Perch, *Perca fluviatilis*, is a handsome fish, first introduced to ponds in Ryde in 1907. A further 300 fish were put into the Cement Works Pond by the River Medina in 1932, and no doubt they have been introduced elsewhere. The Miller's Thumb or Bullhead, *Cottus gobio*, is a common native fish found in most swift flowing streams, using their spiny ventral fins to prevent their being swept away by the current.

Marine species include the Sea Bass, Sea Bream (2), Red Mullet (2), Bogue, Wrasses (5), Sea Bullheads (3), Gurnards (4), Angler, Lumpsucker, Sea Snails (2), Gobies (3), John Dory, Boar-fish, Pilot-fish, Scad, Red band-fish,

(Above) The Common Eel, *Anguilla anguilla*, caught in a land-locked pond by the Military Road near Atherfield.

(Below) The Crucian Carp, *Carassius carassius*, is found in many ponds in the Island.

Mackerel, Weevers (2), Tompot, Shanny, Butter-fish.

Cod Family. There are no fresh water representatives of this family, which includes the Cod, Haddock, Pout, Power-cod, Coal-fish, Whiting, Pollack, Hake, Fork-beard, Ling, 3-, 4-, and 5-bearded Rocklings, Turbot, Brill, Common Topknot, Megrim, Plaice, Dabs (2), Flounder, Soles (2) and Thickback.

Mullet Family. Also only marine species, including Grey Mullets (2), Sand-eel (2), Atherine and Garfish.

Stickleback Family. Three-spined Stickleback *Gasterosteus aculeatus*, is the commonest species. The male assumes bright colours in the breeding season and builds a nest.

The Ten-Spined Stickleback, *Pygosteus pungitius*, is not so common, but found in both east and west Wight. Smaller than the last, the male turns black when excited. Also builds nest and guards the young until they get out of control.

The only marine species is the 15-spined Stickleback, which may enter rivers.

Pipe-fish Family. Only found in the sea, including Pipe-fish (4) and a very occasional Sea-horse has been recorded.

Sun-fish Family. Only two marine species, the Globe Fish and Sun-fish.

Sturgeon Family. The Sturgeon, *Acipensa sturio*, is included on the strength of a single specimen caught in the River Medina 100 years ago.

Eel Family. Young Eels, or elvers, *Anguilla anguilla*, enter our streams in great numbers from the sea, having crossed the Atlantic from the breeding grounds in the Sargasso Sea. Well-grown specimens may be found in rivers and even ponds, but there is some doubt now whether the adults ever do make the journey back to the Sargasso Sea to breed. The Marine Conger Eel is a different species and does not enter rivers.

Carp Family. In contrast, the members of this family are all found in fresh water. It is interesting to note that Sticklebacks are often miscalled 'minnows' in the Island. The true Minnow, *Phoxinus phoxinus*, , which belongs to this family, is not found in the Island, although it is the commonest fish in the rivers and streams on the main-

Common Rudd, *Scardinius erythrophthalmus*. Note the protruding lower jaw.

land opposite. The species to be met here are:

The Carp, *Cyprinus carpio*, probably introduced by monks in the 14th century, includes a number of varieties, such as the Golden Carp, with hardly any scales at all. They all seem to grow to a large size.

The Crucian Carp, *Carassius carassius*, does not have barbels, and is found in many ponds. The Goldfish, *Carassius auratus*, is frequently introduced and breeds regularly. The fry do not take on their golden colour until they are about a year old, and some remain uncoloured looking very much like Crucian Carp.

The Rudd, *Scardinius erythrophthalmus*, is a handsome fish with red fins and eyes, often almost too common in some ponds. It has its dorsal fin set back, and the lower jaw protruding, giving it a pugnacious appearance.

The Roach, *Rutilus rutilus*, is somewhat similar to the Rudd, but has the dorsal fin set further forward, almost level with the ventrals, and the upper jaw is more prominent, giving it a gentler appearance.

The Dace, *Leuciscus leuciscus*, is a graceful fish, happier in streams rather than ponds. It is plentiful in the Eastern Yar and the River Medina.

The Golden Orfe, *Idus idus*, a lovely fish, has been introduced into private ponds and thrives well, although it has not bred.

The Tench, *Tinca tinca*, is probably commoner than realised, as they are not often seen, preferring to keep to the bottom. They are normally dark green, but a lovely golden variety occurs.

The Bream, *Abramis brama*, was introduced in 1907 and was reported to do well.

The Loach, *Nemacheilus barbatula*, is common in the Eastern Yar and Medina.

Pike Family. The Pike, *Esox lucius*, has been introduced.

Salmon Family. The Salmon, *Salmo salar*, does not unfortunately favour our rivers, although it passes up Southampton Water to enter the Itchen and other Hampshire rivers.

The Brown Trout, *Salmo trutta*, is still found in many streams and ponds.

The Rainbow Trout, *Salmo irideus*, has been introduced for commercial fish-farming.

The Grayling, *Thymallus thymallus*, was introduced in 1907, but dropped downstream and did not prosper.

CYCLOSTOMATA (Roundmouths). These include the Lampern, or River Lamprey, *Lampreta fluviatilis*, and the Sea Lamprey, *Petromyzon marinus*, both of which enter our main rivers to breed. They are somewhat eel-like in appearance, but are without paired fins, with a slimy skin without scales and a mouth that is a round sucker with no jaws, but armed with horny teeth. They have 7 pairs of gill openings behind the eyes.

SEVEN

Insects

The insects form the largest Class, *Insecta*, in the largest Phylum, *Arthropoda* (joint-legged animals) of the Animal Kingdom. Like all other arthropods, the insects have an external skeleton, which has to be shed at intervals during growth and, like a suit of armour, has obvious joints in the limbs. They are distinguished from other classes in the phylum by having three pairs of legs, compound eyes and one pair of antennae, with body usually divided into three sections, head, thorax and abdomen.

Undoubtedly, the insects which have received most attention from naturalists and are at the same time most familiar to the general public are the Lepidoptera (scale-winged insects), or butterflies and moths. So far as the butterflies are concerned, we have about 50 species in the Island, of which three are Red Book Data species, and a further 11 are nationally rare. Our Island speciality is the Glanville Fritillary, *Melitaea cinxia*, which is not found anywhere else in the British Isles. It seems to be at the northernmost limit of its range on the south coast of the Island. Visitors to Brook and Compton in spring and late summer have been known to complain of all these spiky black caterpillars with red hears crawling over the cliffs, little realising that they were witnessing a sight denied to anyone else in Britain. It was not always so restricted in its distribution, as it was named after a Lady Glanville, who collected butterflies in the late 18th century, and whose will was contested by her relations on the grounds of insanity. It is doubtful if she ever visited the Island, as the butterfly was found at that time in a number of places on the mainland, but it has long since disappeared from these localities. It is still found in the Channel Islands and in France. The food plants of the caterpillar is the Ribwort Plantain, *Plantago lan-*

Caterpillars of the Island speciality, the Glanville Fritillary Butterfly, *Melitaea cinxia*, in their web on the cliff top at Chilton Chine in April (see colour section for the butterfly).

ceolata, which is common everywhere, so there must be special climatic reasons for its being confined to the coast.

The Island is good for fritillaries, generally. The Dark Green Fritillary, *Argynnis aglaja*, is found on the downs and the Silver-washed Fritillary, *Argynnis paphia*, in woods, particularly as Newtown. The Small Pearl-bordered Fritillary, *Bolania selene*, and the commoner Pearl-bordered Fritillary, *Bolonia euphrosyne*, are both found in reasonable numbers in Parkhurst Forest. The High Brown Fritillary, *Argynnis adippe*, was recorded in the 1950's at Cranmore and Hamstead, and more recently at Newtown, while the Marsh Fritillary, *Euphydryas aurinia*, was also recorded at Cranmore, as well as Parkhurst

Speckled Wood, *Pararge aegeria*, is common in woodland rides.

The White Admiral, *Limenitis camilla*, in Walter's Copse, Newtown.

Forest, in the 1950's, but has not been recorded since 1956, and is now believed to be extinct. The Queen of Spain Fritillary, *Argynnis lathonia*, is a scarce migrant, which was recorded at Nettlestone and at Osborne in 1944, but no further record since. Although often incorrectly referred to as a fritillary, the Duke of Burgundy, *Hamearis lucina*, maintains a steady population on small downland sites, where its food plant, the Cowslip, *Primula veris*, is plentiful.

The blue butterflies are particularly well represented on the Island. The Common Blue, *Polyommatus icarus*, is far and away the most widespread, but the Chalkhill Blue, *Lysandra coridon*, the Small Blue, *Cupido minimus*, and the brilliant Adonis Blue, *Lysandra bellargus*, are all holding their own on the downland, particularly on the south-facing slopes of Afton Down.

The Island is well placed to receive migrants, the best known of which is the Clouded Yellow, *Colias croceus*, which, in some years, arrives in such numbers for it to be called a 'Clouded Yellow Year'. Such a year was 1947, and they were in fairly good numbers in 1949. 1956 and 1964, after which they were hardly seen until 1983, which was quite exceptional with large drifts of Clouded Yellows in all parts of the Island, even in the towns. The Painted Lady, *Cynthia cardui*, is a more regular migrant, appearing surprisingly early in the year on occasions, while the rare American Painted Lady, *Cynthia virginiensis*, was recorded at Freshwater in 1956. Both the Large White, *Pieris brassicae*, and the Small White, *Pieris rapae*, have a residential population, which is boosted by regular migrations from the Continent in summer. On one occasion the keeper at the Needles Lighthouse reported seeing them in such numbers that it appeared to be snowing.

When it comes to moths, we encounter the major difficulty of enormous numbers of species, as is common to many groups of insects. Including the micro-moths, which many naturalists ignore, we have recorded 1,278 species of moths in the Island, which is more than half the known British species. Six of these are Red Data Book species, while a further 56 are nationally rare. Once again, we have our own specialities, not found elsewhere in Britain, including the Isle of Wight Wave, *Idaea humiliata*, resident at Rosehall Green, Freshwater. When Dr K. G. Blair retired from being Deputy Keeper of Entomology at the British Museum (Natural History), he came to live at Freshwater and naturally wished to acquaint himself with the Isle of Wight Wave. He was enquiring the whereabouts of Rosehall Green from the postman in Freshwater Bay, when he was overheard by the local boatman, Herbie Cotton, who broke in and said, 'You want Rosehall Green? I'll take you there. Hop in', indicating his rowing boat. Much taken aback, Dr Blair did as he was told and, in no time at all, they were out of the Bay and along under the chalk cliffs of Tennyson Down.

'There it is. There's Rosehall Green', said Herbie, indicating a large patch of green half way up the cliff at its highest point. It was quite inaccessible from cliff-top or below. The moth hasn't been encountered for many years and has been pronounced extinct, but in such a situation, I am loth to write it off completely.

Within a short time of arriving at Freshwater in 1945, Dr Blair recorded another moth new to Britain in Freshwater marsh. This was Blair's Wainscot, *Sedina buettneri*, which had an unhappy history in that it was grossly over-collected and eventually, in 1952, the marsh was drained and the moth's food plant, lesser

The Isle of Wight Wave Moth, *Idaea humiliata*, confined to the Island.

Blair's Wainscot, *Sedina buettneri*, from Freshwater Marsh.

pond-sedge, *Carex acutiformis*, was burnt by the then Rural District Council, so that it has not been seen since. Dr Blair also recorded Blair's Mocha, *Cyclophora puppillaria*, which is regarded as a very scarce migrant and has since been recorded elsewhere on the mainland in central southern England. Yet another find by Dr Blair was Blair's Shoulder Knot, *Lithophane leautieri*, first recorded at Freshwater in 1951. The larvae feed on the flower buds and foliage of the Monterey Cypress, *Cupressus macrocarpa*, which is a commonly introduced evergreen, so that it spread rapidly in the Island and on the mainland during the 1960's. From all this it will be seen that Freshwater is a mecca for the lepidopterist, as there are several species which are nationally rare to be found in Freshwater marsh and on the downs, and, who knows, how many more still to find?

Mention must also be made of the Reddish Buff, *Acosmetia caliginosa*, which used to be found in the New Forest, but is now only found on the Island. It is a protected species and, until recently, numbers have been at a low level, but it is now being reared and re-introduced to areas where it was previously well known. Its food plant is the saw-wort, *Serratula tinctoria*, found in bushy places and open woods.

Undoubtedly, the most useful aid to the study and recording of moths is the portable moth trap, which consists of a bright light, usually a mercury vapour lamp, to attract the moths, and a glass-topped box, into which the moths fall, so that they may readily be examined and identified, before being set free unharmed. Regular moth-trapping evenings are held by the Entomological Section of the Isle of Wight Natural History and Archaeological Society, and an impressive list of moths caught in various sites was published by J. M. Cheverton and C. N. Pelham (1989), while the Moth Recorder is P. Cramp, Stone Cross Cottage, Godshill I.W. One doesn't need to have a moth trap. By turning on the light in a room and opening the window, one will attract a good selection of moths, which will settle on the wall and may be identified with the aid of a book.

Of particular interest are the large and handsome *Sphingidae*, or Hawk Moths, which are well represented in the Island. There are several resident species, of which the moths or their caterpillars may be encountered. In addition there are migrants, such as the Convolvulus Hawk Moth, *Agrius conolvuli*, the striking Deathshead Hawk, *Acherontia atropos*, with the image of a skull on its thorax and attracted by potatoes, and the Hummingbird Hawk, *Macroglossum stellatarum*, which may be seen hovering over flowers, while sucking up the nectar through a long tube-like proboscis.

Of equal beauty and interest are the *Odonata*, or Dragonflies and Damselflies, of which the Island has 23 species currently recorded, with older records of a further three species not confirmed recently (J. M. Cheverton, 1988). They have been aptly referred to as the bird-watcher's insects, as they may be watched like birds with a pair of binoculars. Although wide-ranging in

Recording catches with the moth trap.

The Golden-ringed Dragonfly, *Cordulegaster boltonii*, at Brighstone.

The Azure Damselfly, *Coenagrion puella*, is the commonest damselfly.

Male Cockchafer, *Melolantha melolantha*, is not nearly so common as it used to be.

their habits, they are most easily seen in the vicinity of suitable ponds and marshes. One can soon discern a pattern in their behaviour, as they tend to come back to the same spot to rest awhile. When it has resumed its flight, then is the time to set up the camera and get it focussed in readiness for its return. Round it comes, just according to plan, and settles – on the camera, which wasn't there before. With patience, however, one can get some marvellous photographs of these beautiful creatures. The handsome blue and green Southern Hawker, *Aeshna cyanea*, is probably our commonest dragonfly, while the larger blue-backed Emperor Dragonfly, *Anax imperator*, and the Broad-bodied Chaser, *Libellula depressa*, with a powder-blue body in the male, are also common and widespread. Damselflies, both brilliant blue and bright red, can be seen dancing over the pond in spring and early summer.

The *Coleoptera* (sheath-winged insects) or beetles form another important order of insects. No fewer than 1,985 species have been recorded in the Island, more than half the known British species, of which 14 are Red Data Book species, and a further 65 species are nationally rare.

They are distinguished from other insects in having their forewings adapted as horny plates, which close over and cover the functional membranous rear wings, when at rest. The Seven-spot Ladybird, *Coccinella septempunctataa*, is a typical beetle and every-one's favourite. At least, that is what I thought until the drought of 1976, when they increased in numbers enormously. I was busy counting the numbers in a cluster of about 200 on the handrail by the steps leading down to the beach at Brook, when a party of visitors came up the steps in a most distressed state. It seemed that they had been set upon by a swarm of ladybirds, and they were biting. They certainly had the marks to show it. I can only assume that the drought conditions had led them to bite in search of liquid, as they are not normally given to this habit. Both adults and larvae feed on aphids (greenfly and blackfly, etc.) so they are very much the gardener's friend.

Other beetles are found in every habitat, except the sea, and exploit all possible food sources. Many are plant feeders, some being wood-borers, while others are predators and parasites, all playing an important part in the economy of nature. The large Stag Beetle,

Lucanus cervus, has been recorded on several occasions at Cowes, and it was assumed that they had flown across the Solent from the New Forest, where they were known to breed. The hurricane of October 1987, felled the trunk of a long dead tree at Cowes, and, in the subsequent cutting-up, three larvae and a pupa of the Stag Beetle were discovered, thus providing the first evidence that breeding actually took place on the Island.

Another large order of insects comprises the Hymenoptera (membrane-winged insects), which include the sawflies, ichneumon flies, wasps, bees and ants. All have two pairs of wings, when present. Although 1,155 species have been recorded in the Island, this is only a small fraction of the total British species, so there is still much work to be done with this interesting group. Red Data Book species total 23, while a further 15 are nationally rare.

The sawflies have no 'waist' and females have the ovipositor (egg-laying organ) adapted as a saw or boring tool, with which they are able to insert their eggs in the stem or leaves of plants. The resulting larvae, which are like caterpillars, feed on the leaves and, in the case of the Gooseberry Sawfly, *Nematus ribesii,* may well defoliate the plants in summer. The Wood Wasp, *Urocerus gigas,* has a long ovipositor which can bore into wood.

The Ichneumon Flies are mainly parasites of the larvae of butterflies and moths, inserting their eggs into the caterpillars with the aid of long and slender ovipositors. They play a vital function in the balance of nature, controlling insect numbers, and are responsible for the destruction of numerous pests. The gall wasps are a specialised group of small winged or wingless wasps, which induce the formation of galls on a variety of plants, as a form of protection and a supply of food for their developing young. They are a fascinating group and well worth a special study. Some species have an alternation of generations, which makes them doubly interesting.

Most species of wasps and bees are solitary. Solitary wasps typically dig a hole or make a cell, into which they place a caterpillar or some such creature immobilised by a sting, and then lay an egg on it before sealing it off. The resulting larva

Wasp Beetle, *Clytus arietis,* is one of the longhorn beetles, which are wood-borers.

Galleries of the Elm Bark Beetle, *Scolytus scolytus,* responsible for carrying the fungus, which causes Elm Disease.

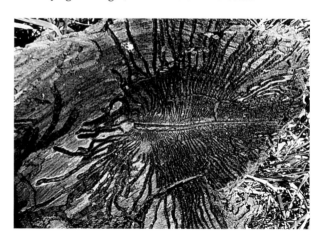

will feed upon the food provided and emerge the following year. In contrast the solitary bees provision their cells with a mixture of nectar and pollen, called 'bee-bread'. The highest development, however, is attained by the truly social insects, the familiar wasps, bees and ants. In all cases they have a matriarchal society, with egg-laying confined to one or more fertile females or queens, while the work is carried out by infertile females, or workers, with varying numbers of males required to fertilise the new queens as may become necessary. As stings are adapted from ovipositors, only female insects can sting.

Wasps construct their nests of paper and feed their young on meat. There is no provision made for the winter, so that in the autumn all the workers and males die and only the newly fertilised females go into hibernation and start new colonies the following spring. Bees feed their young on pollen and nectar, but bumble bees only provide a waxen honey-pot for the occasional wet day and, like wasps, die off in the winter, except for the hibernating queens, and start afresh each year.

The Honey Bee, *Apis mellifera*, stores pollen and honey in wax combs, so that the colony can survive in winter. Ants, on the other hand, are the most highly developed of all, being the farmers of the insect world. There are no solitary ants, and they live in communal nests, which may contain several queens. They are known to cultivate beds of fungi in their nests and tend herds of aphids like cattle, from which they obtain drops of sweet 'honey-dew', when stroked by their antennae. There is considerable division of labour and one species actually raids the nest of another species and makes slaves of its captives. Some 29 species have been recorded in the Island, of which five are Red Data Book species. Mr R. Snow has been carrying out a survey during the last few years and has confirmed the presence of 19 species, leaving 10 species still to be accounted for, so there is a nice little task for someone to undertake.

The Orthoptera (straight-winged insects) include the cockroaches, earwigs, groundhoppers, grasshoppers, bush-crickets and crickets, which are all well represented on the Island. Four species of cockroaches have been recorded, of which two are introductions. Four species of earwigs have been recorded. All three British species of Ground-hoppers occur, but have not been thoroughly mapped. The slipped cliffs at Compton Bay, as well as Alum Bay, are good places to find them. The grasshoppers, bush-crickets and crickets have been well surveyed by D. G. Rands, and it is hoped that the distribution maps will be published shortly. A selection of these are reproduced here, from which the

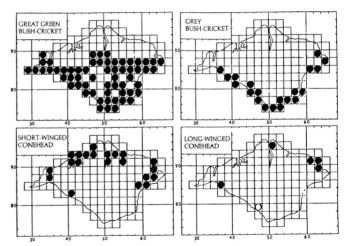

Distribution Maps of Bush-crickets in the Isle of Wight to January, 1990. Great Green Bush-cricket, see text; Grey Bush Cricket is clearly a coastal species; Short-winged Conehead, *Conocephalus dorsalis*, is an estuarine species; Long-winged Conehead, *Conocephalus discolor*, is rare.

Distribution Maps of Crickets and Grasshoppers in the Isle of Wight to January, 1990. Wood Cricket, *Nemobius sylvestris*, is a woodland species; Common Green Grasshopper, *Omocestus viridulus*, is mostly found on the chalk downs; Lesser Marsh Grasshopper, *Chorthippus albomarginatus*, is clearly an estuarine species; The Mottled Grasshopper. *Myrmeleotettix maculatus*, is mostly found on heathland.

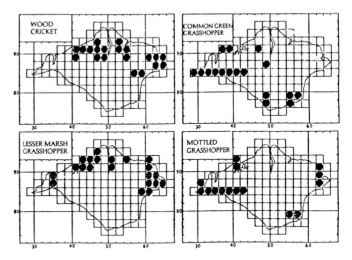

variable distribution of species may be determined. It will be noted that the handsome Great Green Bush-cricket, *Tettigonia viridissima*, is not found on the tertiary clays in the north of the Island, as the well-drained chalk and greensands in the south are more likely to ensure the survival of the eggs, which are laid in the soil, over

(Above) Grey Bush Cricket, *Platycleis denticulata*, is confined to the south coast of the Island.

(Left) The Wood Cricket, *Nemobius sylvestris*, is a good indicator of old woodland.

(Below) The Field Grasshopper, *Chorthippus brunneus*, is the commonest grasshopper, being found in every tetrad in the Island.

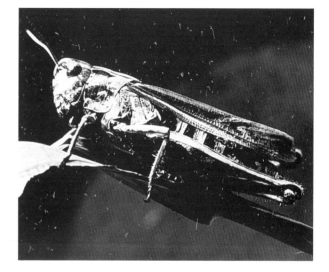

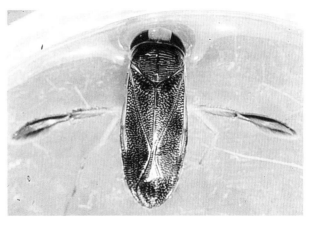

(Above) Lesser Water Boatman, *Corixa punctata*, is frequent in ponds.

(Left) Cepero's Groundhopper, *Tetrix ceperoi*, from Compton Bay.

(Below) Back-swimmer, *Notonecta glauca*, is common in ponds.

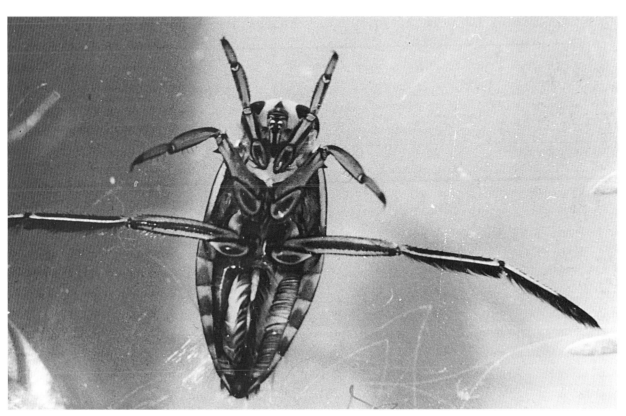

the winter. In addition to those shown, it is worth noting that the Stripe-winged Grasshopper, *Stenobothrus lineatus*, is confined to the downs at Ventnor. The strange Mole-cricket, *Gryllotalpa gryllotalpa*, with front legs enlarged for digging, like a mole, has been recorded on a number of occasions in different parts of the Island, and one never knows where it might turn up next. It makes a whirring sound like that of a nightjar, but more inward. The Field Cricket, *Gryllus campestris*, used to be common on the downs above Newchurch. The Wart-biter, *Decticus verrucivorus*, was recorded once on St Boniface Down in 1951 (D. R. Ragge, 1973). Roesel's Bush-cricket, *Metrioptera roeselii*, has been recently recorded from Newtown.

The *Diptera* (insects with two wings, when present) include true flies, such as house-flies, bluebottles, horse-flies, hover-flies, crane-flies, mosquitoes, gnats and midges. There are over 5,000 British species, of which only 608 have been recorded in the Island. Ten are Red Data Book species, while a further 63 are nationally rare. Once one has got over one's natural prejudices, it is nice to find that members of this order have many varied forms and interesting life histories. The Hover-flies are masters of the art of mimicry. Although completely harmless themselves, they cunningly assume the appearance of bees and wasps and so derive protection from their enemies. They also, like ladybirds, feed on aphids, so should be encouraged.

The *Hemiptera* (half-winged insects) include the true bugs, with usually two pairs of wings, the front ones partly hardened, but not encasing the rear wings completely, as in the beetles. Examples are the shield-bugs, common on plants, the frog-hoppers, whose nymphs make cuckoo-spit, leaf-hoppers, aphids, water boatmen, or back-swimmer in ponds, where the Water Scorpion, *Nepa cinerea*, and the Water-measurer, *Hydrometra stagnorum*, may also be seen. A total of 382 species have been recorded in the Island, which is about a quarter of the known British species. Two are Red Data Book species, while a further 15 are nationally rare.

This still leaves a number of small groups of insects, which have been sadly neglected, such as the wingless bristle-tails and spring-tails, mayflies, lice, fleas, lacewings, alderflies, snake flies and caddis flies. Each of these groups is crying out for someone to take a special interest in it, and so increase our knowledge of Island natural history. What about it?

EIGHT

Other Arthropods

Other Classes within the Phylum *Arthropoda* include the crustaceans, centipedes, millipedes and spiders and their allies. Work carried out recently by A. N. Keay, a prison officer at Albany Prison, has been a major contribution to our knowledge of these groups. It just goes to show what single-minded determination can achieve.

The *Crustacea* (Hard-shelled animals), which some biologists now regard as a Phylum on its own, differ from insects in having more than three pairs of legs and two pairs of antennae. They are mostly water-dwelling creatures and are only represented on land by the woodlice. These familiar creatures are contained within the group *Isopoda* (equal-footed crustaceans), which still retain a series of plates, known as lung-books, similar to gills for the purpose of breathing, so that they must live in damp places. Fourteen species have been recorded in the Island, of which two rare species are worthy of mention. *Porcellionides pruinosus* was recorded by Morey (1909) in garden waste at Newport and recent records seem to confirm that it is confined to gardens, whereas *Miktoniscus patiencei* has been recorded from a saltmarsh, but there are insufficient data to be certain that it is confined to this habitat. The large Sea Slater, *Ligia oceanica*, hides under rocks and seaweed on the upper shore by day and becomes active by night, while the Pill-bug, *Armadillidium vulgare*, which is able to roll itself into a ball, is found mostly on the chalk downs. In ponds the closely related Water Hog-louse, *Asellus aquaticus*, is common, especially when the water is stagnant. The *Amphipoda* (with legs adapted for walking and swimming) include the Freshwater Shrimp, *Gammarus pulex*, which is abundant in our chalk streams amongst

Sea Slater, *Ligia oceanica*, may be seen active at night on the upper shore by torchlight.

Water Hog-louse, *Asellus aquaticus*, is found in ponds and ditches.

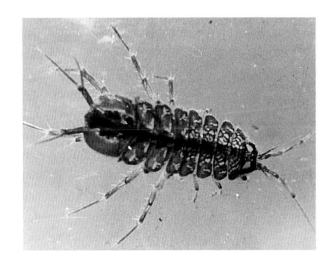

Water-cress, *Rorippa nasturtium-aquaticum*, and the Sand-hopper, *Talitrus saltator*, common under rotting seaweed on the upper shore. Another species worthy of mention is *Gammarus insen-*

Broad-clawed Porcelain Crab, *Porcellana platycheles*, will be found hiding under rocks at low tide.

sibilis, which has been found in a brackish saltern at Newtown. This is an extremely rare species now protected under the Wildlife and Countryside Act 1981. Newtown is the only site known in the Island, and it is restricted to a few other similar habitats on the mainland. Morey (1909) recorded seven species, but this has been increased to 53 species by Collins *et al.* (1990). Other crustaceans found in fresh water include a host of small species generally referred to as 'water-fleas', such as *Cypris* spp., *Cyclops* spp., and *Daphnia* spp., which have been little studied on the Island.

It is in the sea, however, that the crustaceans attain their greatest diversity and highest development, occupying much the same position of importance as the insects do on land. The *Decapoda* (ten-legged crustaceans) include the prawns, shrimps, lobsters, squat lobsters and crabs, of which Morey (1909) recorded 30 species, but this has been much enlarged by recent work, which is still in progress. One only has to watch a hermit crab, *Eupagurus bernhardus*, undertaking the risky business of exchanging its protective shell for another larger one, or consider how the Spider Crab, *Hyas araneus*, ensures protective camouflage by actually planting seaweeds on its carapace, and the phenomenon of autotomy, the voluntary severing of a limb with subsequent regrowth, to realise that they are a particularly rewarding group of animals to study in depth.

The *Cirripedia* (curl-footed crustaceans) include the barnacles of various kinds. The commonest of these is the Acorn Barnacle, *Balanus balanoides*, which is often seen in enormous numbers closely attached to rocks on the shore. One might well wonder how such dissimilar creatures can be in the same class as crabs and lobsters, but in fact the larval stage of the barnacle is similar to that of other crustaceans and is free-swimming. In due course, however, it attaches itself to a rock by the neck and grows horny plates round its body for protection, with two movable plates in the centre, which it is able to open when the tide is in and sweep its feathery legs through the water to catch food, which is passed to the mouth. Having become fixed, it remains there for life, and reproduction is carried out by the simultaneous discharge of both eggs and sperm into the water at a specific period during the year. The resulting fertilised eggs develop into mobile free-swimming larvae, which are an important constituent of animal plankton, which is an important food source for many animals. Eight species of rock barnacles have been recorded in the Island, including a foreign species from Australia, *Elminius modestus*, which is well established. Two species of *Chthamalus* have their easterly limits in the Island. *C. stellatus* at Hanover Point Brook, and *C. montagui* at Bonchurch. The stalked Ship barnacle, *Lepas anatifera*, found in clusters attached to flotsam,

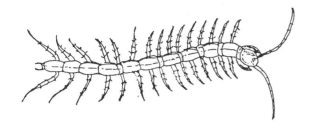

Lithobius forficatus, the most widely distributed Centipede in the Island.

Trachyspaera lobata, a millipede new to Britain found at Bembridge in 1984, only 4mm long.

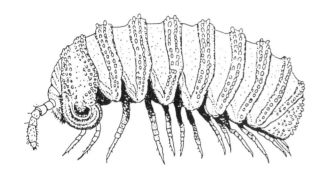

is occasionally washed up, particularly in the autumn. In addition there is a strange member of this group, *Sacculina carcina*, which, like the others, starts life as a free-swimming larva, but attaches itself under the tail of a crab and degenerates into a bean-shaped bag with long outgrowths which ramify through the body of the host, upon which it feeds as a parasite. This is not to be confused with the egg-mass of the crab, which is carried in the same position, but is quite obviously granular.

The *Myriapoda* (many-footed arthropods) include the centipedes and millipedes, although in neither case do they have anything like the numbers of legs indicated by their names.

The *Chilopoda* (lip-footed) comprises the centipedes, which have a more of less flattened body with one pair of legs per segment. They are carnivorous and generally regarded as beneficial. Morey (1909) recorded only 6 species, which A. N. Keay has now increased to no less than 30 species, of which ten are nationally rare. These

include *Pachymerium ferrugineum*, from coastal shingle, of which there have been only three British records, *Nothogeophilus turki*, which was described as new to science in 1989 and has only been recorded from the Scilly Isles, the coastal cliffs at Freshwater Bay and the saltmarsh at Newtown, and *Lithobius tricuspis*, which has only been found in woodlands, fields and hedges in South Devon and Carmarthenshire, apart from the Island.

The *Chilognatha* (lip-jawed) or *Diplopoda* (double-footed) comprise the millipedes, which have two pairs of legs per segment and are herbivorous, so many do a certain amount of damage in the garden. Morey (1909) recorded five species, which have now been increased by A. N. Keay to 22 species, of which three are rare and a further nine are local. Of particular interest is *Trachyspaera lobata*, described by A. N. Keay (1988) and found in coastal woodland at Bembridge, with only three known sites worldwide.

The *Arachnida*, consisting of spiders, harvestmen, pseudoscorpions and mites, are a particularly interesting class. Of the 584 species of spiders found in Britain Morey (1909) listed 153 recorded in the Island, while Wm A. Falconer (1930) increased this total to 219 species, and Dr A. F. Millidge (1959), a leading authority on spiders, who came from Newport, brought the total to 282, a number which he considered could be easily increased by careful searching throughout the year. Some new species have, in fact, been recorded, including the handsome *Argiope bruennichi*, a Mediterranean species, which was released near Bournemouth in the 1940's and was first recorded on the Island at Hamstead in August, 1979, since when it has turned up in a number of places complete with cocoons, showing that it is breeding on the Island and is likely to become increasingly common. The female is very large with black and yellow bars across its abdomen. The male is small, brown and insignificant.

An even more exciting find was that by Paul Hillyard, of the British Museum (Natural History), who discovered a considerable population of the theridiid spider, *Episinus maculipes*, at St Lawrence in 1983. This spider was accepted for the British list on the strength of a single female specimen caught at Tiptree Heath, Essex, in 1929, so a British male from St. Lawrence was able to be described for the first time. Unfortunately there are not enough people in the field who have the ability to identify spiders for any distribution maps to be compiled, and much remains to be learnt about their biology and habits. What is known, however, shows that they are full of interest. They are found in every habitat and one can gain some idea of their importance when one considers that the weight of insects and other prey consumed by spiders annually in this country substantially exceeds the weight of the human population. It is well worth stopping to watch spiders at work, whether it is in the complex task of making a web, or catching and immobilising prey. One cannot fail to be impressed by their ingenuity.

Harvestmen differ from spiders in having a body all in one piece, two eyes only and long legs. Morey (1909) listed nine species, which have been increased to 12 by A. N. Keay, including three rare species, *Dicranopalpus ramosus*, found in association with man and his dwellings, *Homalenotus quadridentatus*, in woodlands and grasslands on the chalk, and *Megabunus diadema*, also found in woodland.

There are no true scorpions represented in this country, but a number of quite harmless false scorpions, or pseudoscorpions, very much like a miniature tailless scorpion, are found. Morey (1909) listed four species, which have been increased to nine by A. N. Keay. These include the rare species, *Neobisium maritimum*, in its most easterly location in Great Britain, *Roncocreagris cambridgei*, another south-western species found in coastland woodlands, *Lamprochernes savignyi* and *L. nodosus*, both found in association with man.

Although a large number of mites occur in the Island, no one has yet set about the task of making a list, so this is something crying out to be done. They are found in all habitats on land, in ponds and in estuaries.

Cave Spider, *Meta menardi*, is found in dark, damp places.

Egg sacs of the Cave Spider.

NINE

Molluscs

Snails and slugs are not everyone's favourites. For myself I recall with pleasure the many years spent in holding snail races at school, when we should have been giving all our attention to a cricket match. My interest was further aroused when I first saw the waves of muscular contraction in the foot of a snail as it glided slowly over a pane of glass. I was intrigued also by their telescopic eyes and the variable makings on their shells, but hairiness was something I did not associate with snails, so when I found a really hairy snail, I was quite certain I had found something new to science. I rushed to my books, only to find that there were several species of hairy snails, especially when young, and they were common and widespread. It wasn't long before I discovered that the only way to tell the difference between some species was by dissecting their reproductory organs, and my interest began to wane somewhat, but I still have a high regard for this group of animals and can recommend them as highly interesting subjects for study. Most molluscs live in the sea, and it is convenient to deal with the marine molluscs separately from the non-marine molluscs, such as snails and slugs, which live on land or in fresh water ponds and brackish water, and first claim our attention.

The Phylum *Mollusca* to which they belong is the next largest and most important phylum after the *Arthropoda*. The name is derived from the Latin *mollis*, meaning soft, referring to their soft bodies without an external skeleton which is a feature of the arthropods. The snails, however, do have a shell, into which the animal can withdraw for protection, and this has the advantage of being continuously added on to during life, instead of having to be shed at regular intervals as in the arthropods. The animal itself consists of a muscular foot, a mantle

Banded Snail, *Cepaea hortensis* or *C. nemoralis*, which are so variable that they can only be reliably told apart from the shape of their love-darts.

covering the internal organs with a respiratory pore leading to the mantle cavity or lung, and head with mouth and one or two pairs of tentacles, one of which contains the primitive eyes. An important feature is the radula, or rasp-like tongue, with which it feeds. The shell is formed by material exuded by the mantle. Most species are hermaphrodite, containing both male and female organs. During courtship, love-darts may be discharged to stimulate further activity resulting in mating, when each transfers sperm to the other, so that some time later each is able to

Even the Common Garden Snail, *Helix aspersa,* can spring a
surprise like this monstrosity "Cornucopia" found at
Freshwater in 1968.

Map showing comparative numbers of species of land
molluscs recorded in each tetrad.

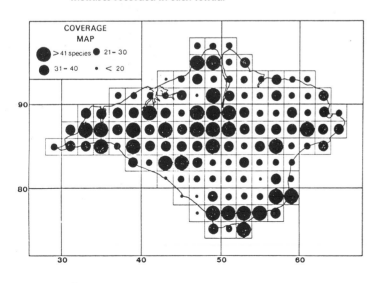

lay fertile eggs, from which miniature editions of
the parents in due course hatch. Snails and slugs
are found in all habitats, but are restricted by the
need to conserve water. They are therefore most
active at night or after rain. Slugs would seem to
be at a disadvantage, lacking a shell into which it
can withdraw, but this is offset by their ability to
burrow deep in the soil or slide into narrow
cracks in rocks or beneath bark. Most species feed
on rotting vegetation, fungi, algae and lichens. A
few species are carnivorous.

The non-marine species of molluscs on the
Island have been well recorded in the past.
Morey (1909) gave details of 96 species, including three brackish water species among the
marine section. Dr R. C. Preece (1980) increased
this total to 115 species, which is more than half
of those found in Britain, although six species
recorded by earlier workers were not confirmed
by the latest survey. A map showing the
comparative numbers of species recorded in each
tetrad is reproduced here and shows well how
favourable the Island is for molluscs. The most
favourable tetrads are those which contain a
variety of habitats, particularly woodland on
chalk or limestone outcrops, with the richest
tetrads having more than 70 species in some

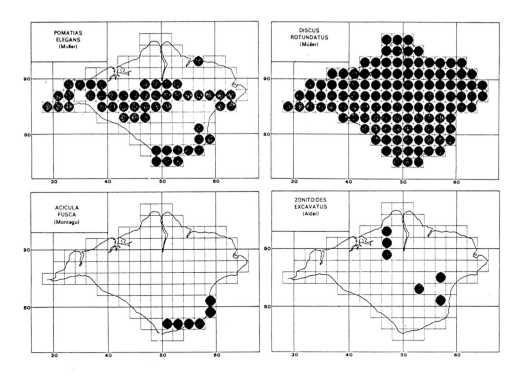

Distribution Maps of Land Molluscs in the Isle of Wight to 1980. (Reproduced from Preece 1980a).

Pomatias elegans, a real calcicole.

cases. Distribution maps were shown for all species and a selection of these is reproduced here. Snails generally favour lime-rich alkaline soils, as lime is necessary for the formation of the shell. Some species, however, are calcicoles, or lime-loving species, being strictly confined to the chalk and tertiary limestone areas, such as *Pomatias elegans*, as shown by its distribution map. In this species the sexes are separate and it is also one of the few land snails to retain a horny operculum, or trap-door, which closes over the mouth of the shell and thus guards against desiccation in the dry conditions in which it lives.

Although everyone is familiar with the common Garden Snail, *Helix aspersa* it may come as some surprise to find that another snail, *Discus rotundatus*, is equally, if not more, common and widespread, and yet hardly known at all. It is a pretty snail with a flat coiled shell only about 6mm across, so is easily overlooked. It is found in moss and ground litter, under stones, etc. Another species, *Acicula fusca*, is strangely confined to the woods in the Undercliff, while *Zonitoides excavatus* is a real calcifuge, or lime-hating species, and is confined to a few areas of

acid woodland as shown on the map. Both these species also have the sexes separate. *Potamopyrgus jenkinsi* is a fresh water snail, which was first recorded at Yarmouth in 1921, since when it has spread rapidly and is now one of the commonest fresh water snails in the Island. In contrast, however, *Helicella itala*, was recorded by Morey (1909) as being plentiful in a number of sites as shown on the map, but Preece (1980) was unable to find any living specimens at all in spite of careful search. Its apparent decline or disappearance form the Island must be seen as a general recession affecting this species over the whole of southern England, as indicated on the distribution map by Kerney (1976). Reasons for this decline are not fully understood, but may well relate to changes in downland vegetation resulting from changes in agricultural practices. It is noteworthy that in central Ireland this species is still common and shows no evidence of decline.

The slug, *Boettgerilla pallens*, was first described in 1912 and first recorded in this country in 1972 at Windermere. A single adult specimen

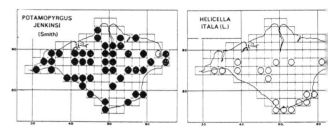

Distribution Maps of Island Specialities in 1980. (Reproduced from Preece, 1980a).

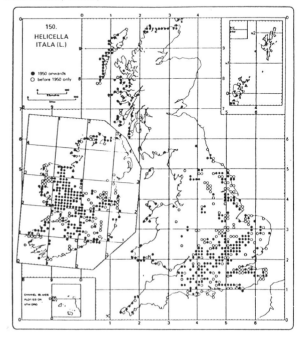

Distribution Map of *Helicella itala* in British Isles. (Reproduced from Kerney, 1976).

Discus rotundatus, is the most widespread land mollusc.

was found in August 1981 by Mrs E. B. Rands under a twig at the entrance to the chalk pit on Shorwell Shute (Preece, 1984). Since then it has been found at a number of sites that had previously been sampled in detail, so this is part of a general spread of this species over Europe.

As in other groups, the Island has its specialities, such as *Vertigo moulinsiana*, a scarce species found in rich calcareous fens and recorded at Freshwater Marsh and Brading. *Truncatellina callicratis britannica* is a sub-species of a widespread continental species with reduced dentition in the shell aperture, only known from a few coastal downland sites in southern England, as shown in the accompanying map. It was recorded from Steephill Cove over a century ago, and Preece (1980) found that it still occurs there

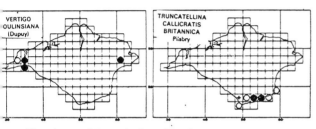

Distribution Maps of selected land molluscs in the Isle of Wight in 1980. (Reproduced from Preece, 1980a).

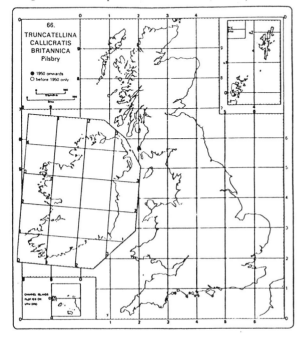

Distribution Map of *Truncatellina callicratis britannica* in the British Isles. (Reproduced from Kerney, 1976).

Census organised by the Conchological Society, the results of which were published in 1980. More recently, Janice Light and Ian Killeen embarked on an intensive survey in 1987, of which initial findings were discussed in a paper in the *Proceedings of the Natural History and Archaeological Society for 1989* (1990) and it is intended that the full results will be published in 1993/4 as *The Marine Mollusca of the Isle of Wight* (in preparation). In the meantime the authors have kindly compiled the following table to show the comparison between those species recorded by Morey (1909) and those found during the current survey.

CLASS (Sub-class)	MOREY (1909)			LIGHT/KILLEEN (1987-)		
	Alive	Dead	Totals	Alive	Dead	Totals
POLYPLACOPHORA	3		3	4		4
GASTROPODA						
Prosobranchia	25	28	53	59	33	92
Opisthobranchia	11	6	17	19		19
Pulmonata	2	1	3	3		3
SCAPHODODA		1	1	1		1
BIVALVIA	22	32	54	41	30	71
CEPHALOPODA	5	1	6	1		1
TOTALS	68	69	137	128	63	191

Pond Snails, *Limnaea palustris* (left) and *Planorbarius corneus* (right).

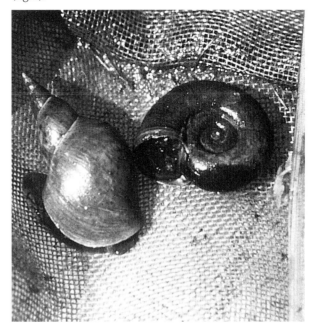

after much hunting. It is only 2mm in height. A fresh water limpet, *Ferrissia wautieri*, that was only discovered living in Britain in 1977, was found in a pond at Stag Lane, Parkhurst (Preece, 1980).

Like the crustaceans, the molluscs attain their greatest diversity and development in the sea, so we must turn our minds to the marine molluscs. Morey (1909) was surprised to find that no previous lists of marine molluscs had been published up to that time. A few species had been included in the Victoria History (1900), but Moreys list of nearly 140 species, being a compilation of his own records and those gleaned from other sources, was the first of its kind for the Isle of Wight. Very little further work was done until L. C. Prebble took part in the Marine

In addition a paper on *The Marine Flora and Fauna of Bembridge and St Helens* by Collins *et al*, in the same *Proceedings*, included an extensive list of molluscs of that particular area with many interesting observations.

By and large, compared with most of southeast England, the Island is generally quite rich in marine molluscs, benefiting by its central position in attracting a number of Atlantic species. The Island also possesses a wide variety of geological deposits and structural features giving rise to many shore types. Also, as an Island, there are both exposed and sheltered shores with consequently different molluscan species. For this reason there is a pronounced north/south faunal divide, with the Solent having a fauna associated with sheltered conditions, siltier substrate and turbid water, while the fauna of the south coast is more that of clear, rocky and more exposed conditions.

The class *Polyplacophora* includes the Chitons or Coat-of-mail Shells, which are the most primitive molluscs. They are distinguished by having a series of eight overlapping plates covering the back, surrounded by a fleshy girdle, looking somewhat like a woodlouse. The under surface is formed by the muscular foot, with which it clings to the rocks. Recent work at Bembridge has increased the number of Island species to five (Collins *et al*, 1990).

Coat-of-mail Shell or Chiton, *Lepidochitona cinereus*.

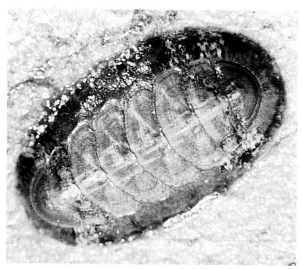

In the class *Gastropoda* (belly-footed), the sub-class *Prosobranchia* includes most of the familiar sea snails with a single shell. The most primitive of these are the limpets, of which the Common Limpet, *Patella vulgata*, is the most familiar. We are lucky, however, to have two other species of *Patella*, *P. depressa* and *P. ulyssiponensis*, which are really Atlantic species, but extend up the Channel to their easterly limit on the Island. The intriguing Keyhole Limpet, *Diodora apertura*, so named because of the 'keyhole' in the top of the shell was recorded by Morey (1909) and I have found specimens at Hanover Point some years ago, but it seems to be getting scarce. Fortunately this is not the case with the lovely Blue-rayed limpet, *Halcion pellucidum*, which is frequently found in pits on the holdfasts and on the fronds of Oarweed off the south coast of the Island, but not in the Solent. The Slipper Limpet, *Crepidula fornicata*, is not a true limpet and looks as though it were half of a bivalve mollusc, but it is a single shell with a shelf, giving it the shape of a slipper.

Diagram of Cup-and-saucer Limpet or Chinaman's Hat, *Calyptraea chinensis*.

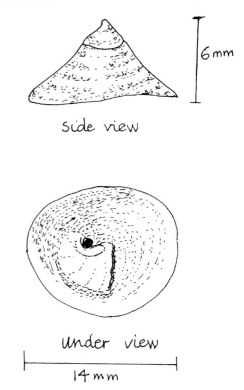

side view

6 mm

under view

14 mm

It forms chains of numerous individuals attached to each other, the youngest on the top being active males, while the oldest at the bottom is the female laying fertilised eggs. Each individual, therefore, starts by being a male and eventually becomes a female when it reaches the bottom of the chain. They were introduced accidentally to the east coast of Britain with oysters from America at the turn of the century and were first recorded off the Island in 1920 by Captain G. C. C. Damant, since when they have increased enormously, so that now at Thorness they are by far the commonest mollusc. They are a serious pest in oyster fisheries as they tend to smother the oysters and compete for food.

There are many kinds of top shells, so called because they resemble the old-fashioned whipping top in shape. The Grey Topshell, *Gibbula cineraria*, is the commonest, but the handsome Painted Topshell, *Calliostoma zizyphinum*, should be looked for. Empty shells may be washed up, but brighter living shells will be found at low water and beyond at Bembridge, where a grey variety, *lyonsii*, is also found. The Purple Topshell, *Gibbula umbilicalis*, seems to be retracting, and can now only be reliably found at Freshwater.

The Edible periwinkle, *Littorina littorea*, is probably the most familiar mollusc and is certainly the most widespread round the Island. The Flat Periwinkle, *Littorina littoralis* group, now divided into *L. obtusata* and *L. mariae*, is also very common on seaweeds, upon which it feeds, with many different colour forms, brown, red, green, orange and yellow, sometimes banded. There is some evidence that under certain conditions the yellow form predominates, whereas under other conditions the dark brown form is dominant, but in the main it seems to be a highly variable species. The Small Periwinkle, *Littorina nerotoides*, might well be missed, as it is not only very small, but occupies a position on the shore that one would not associate with marine molluscs. It is found in great numbers on rocks in the splash zone above high water mark, usually in crevices, feeding on lichens, but they are rare on the Solent coast. Unlike the others we have mentioned, this is a lung-breather and is well on the

Painted Topshells, *Calliostoma zizyphinum*.

Sting Winkle, *Ocenebra erinacea*, drills holes in oyster shells. It is really a whelk.

Great Scallop, *Pecten maximus*, off Bembridge.

way to becoming a land mollusc.

The large shell of the Buckie or Common Whelk, *Buccinum undatum,* is another common object of the seashore, together with its egg-mass, rather like a sponge. The smaller Dog-whelk, *Nucella lapillus,* is most likely to be found in association with barnacles on which it feeds, but in recent years Dog-whelks have suffered greatly from the effects of tributyltin (TBT) used in marine anti-fouling paint, which has significantly reduced the reproductive potential of the animal. The effect on Dog-whelk populations has been widespread around the whole of the United Kingdom. In the Island the species is still frequent on many south coast shores, but there have been no records from the northern shores in recent years (Herbert, 1989).

The *Opisthobranchia* include the sea-slugs, some of which are highly coloured and most attractive. The largest is the Common Grey Sea-slug, *Aeolodia papillosa,* which feeds on the Snakelocks Sea-anemone, *Anemonia viridis,* from which it extracts the sting-cells and uses them for its own protection. It may be seen at Bembridge in the spring laying its white ribbons of eggs in the rock pools. The Sea-hare, *Aplysia punctata,* so called because its tentacles are shaped like a hare's ears, is most likely to be encountered at Freshwater. When frightened, it emits a purple dye into the water for protection.

Section of boat's keel, which has been burrowed by the Ship Worm, *Teredo navalis*, which is a specialised mollusc.

The *Pulmonata* are in the main small snails, which have developed a lung for breathing and are usually found on the upper shore or in estuaries.

The *Scaphopoda* include but a single species, the Elephant's Tusk Shell, *Dentalium entalis*, which is a simple hollow tubular shell like a miniature elephant's tusk. Empty shells may most frequently be found intact at Seaview.

The *Bivalvia* consist of molluscs with two shells hinged together. The Common Mussel, *Mytilus edulis*, is a typical example and very widespread in the Island. There are a number of scallops, of which the largest, the Great Scallop, *Pecten maximus*, is found off Bembridge. The smaller Variegated Scallop, *Chlamys varia*, is also common, as is the Queen Scallop, *Chlamys opercularis*, which swims by rapidly opening and closing its shells. The native Oyster, *Ostrea edulis*, is still frequent in the Solent, in spite of the Slipper Limpets already mentioned. The oyster fishery at Newtown faced disaster in 1963, when the prolonged severe frost killed the oysters put down in the Clamerkin river and consequently contaminated the bed of the river. Fortunately, it was just at that time that it was discovered that a larger bivalve, the American Clam, *Mercenaria mercenaria*, which must have been thrown overboard from an American liner, had taken to breeding in the warm water outflow from Marchwood power station on Southampton Water. As these were polluted waters, they would not have been fit for human consumption, but Cyril Lucas, in collaboration with the Minister of Agriculture, Fisheries and Food, devised a system whereby they were collected and put down in the river at Newtown for a time, before being put through a series of cleansing tanks until

Eggs of the Cuttlefish, *Sepia officinalis.*

Collection of shells. How many can you name?

they were deemed fit to eat, resulting in a profitable trade, particularly with France.

Mud dwellers, such as the Edible Cockle, *Cerastoderma edule*, appear to be confined to the Solent. The Razor Shell, *Ensis ensis* and *E. siliqua*, burrow in sand and need a cleaner environment, but they, too, suffered enormous losses in the severe winter of 1962/3, from which they have still not recovered. Some bivalves are adapted for rock-boring, such as the Common Piddock, *Pholas dactylus*, which leads a solitary life imprisoned in a bore-hole of its own making. The Ship Worm, *Teredo navalis*, bores into wood and can cause great damage to the keels of wooden boats moored in our harbours and estuaries.

The *Cephalopods* include the cuttlefish, squids and octopus, which are all highly developed molluscs, of which we have some six species. The commonest is the Common Cuttlefish, *Sepia officinalis*, which, like the Sea-hare already mentioned and the Octopus, *Octopus vulgaris*, discharges a dark ink into the water to effect its escape from its enemies. It has a remarkable power of instant colour change and may take on the colour and patterning of its background. It can move swiftly by ejecting water through a funnel formed by the muscular foot, providing a means of 'jet-propulsion'. The most remarkable feature of this group of molluscs, however, is the high development of the eyes, which are as elaborate and efficient as the human eye.

It will be seen, therefore, that the molluscs are a most diverse group of animals, largely owing to the manner in which the foot, body and mantle, together with the shell, are modified to suit particular needs. Not only do we have all this diversity ready to hand on our seashores, but, because of their hard shells which fossilize well, we have encapsulated in our cliffs that invaluable fossil record showing the evolutionary history of molluscs for the past 120 million years.

TEN

Other Invertebrates

When animal life first began to evolve from the first single-celled organisms such as *Amoeba*, certain basic plans were followed. The *Porifera*, or sponges, are the simplest of multicellular animals, consisting of two layers of cells, supported by a fibrous or flinty skeleton, surrounding a central cavity. The inner cells have many vibrating hairs, or *cilia*, which draw a current of water through numerous pores into the central cavity, where food and oxygen are taken in and waste materials pass out through a large pore, or *osculum*. The real bath-sponge is the fibrous skeleton of a tropical species, but none of our sponges approaches this in shape or form. Morey (1909) listed only six species, but recent work carried out at Bembridge has resulted in 31 species being recorded (Collins *et al*, 1990). Many are small and hard to identify, but one should recognise the Purple Sponge, *Grantia compressa*, like grey or yellow flat purses hanging down from rocks amongst seaweeds, the encrusting Bread-crumb Sponge, *Halichondrea panicea*, attached to rocks, like a miniature moonscape with extinct volcanoes, which are, in fact, the *oscula*, usually coloured green, but may be yellow or orange, and the small yellow-orange Boring Sponge, *Cliona celata*, which lives in holes it has excavated in limestone or discarded shells. One will frequently find oyster shells riddled with holes made by the Boring Sponge.

The *Coelenterata* (with hollow intestine), containing a single body cavity, include the fresh water *Hydra*, of which there are several species, marine hydroids or sea-firs, jellyfish, sea-anemones, corals, etc. They are amongst the commonest of marine animals and are typically based on a circular plan with radial symmetry, often very like flowers. The hydroids are colonial, consisting of many individual animals with a single body cavity surrounded by tentacles containing stinging cells, held on a supporting branching skeleton of characteristic and plant-like shape. They may often be mistaken for seaweeds, but lack colour and, when pressed, they do not adhere to the paper.

The Portuguese Man-of-War, *Physalia physalis*, is occasionally cast ashore on the south coast of the Island. It is rather like a large jellyfish, but in reality it is a complicated colony of individual animals of different kinds, some for feeding, some for attack, some for defence, some for reproduction, some for suspension and others for movement. It floats by means of a gas-filled pale blue bladder, about 6ins. long, from which a mass of tentacles many feet long hang down. The stinging cells are very powerful, so they should not be touched. The smaller related By-the-wind-sailor, *Velella velella*, was found cast ashore near Grange Chine, Brighstone, by Mr and Mrs F. Sykes in October, 1986 (R. Herbert, 1988).

The *Scyphozoa* (cup-like animals) include the true jellyfishes, the commonest of which, *Aurelia aurita*, with four pale violet crescents, sometimes occurs in enormous numbers. I well remember finding myself swimming in the sea with a texture of tapioca pudding, so numerous were the jellyfish. Dr David Biggs reported up to 200 Compass Jellyfish, *Chrysaora hysoscella*, with a brown spot in the centre and 24 brown triangular patches radiating from it, as well as 30 even larger species, *Rhizostoma octopus*, with a purple-fringed bell, washed up at Totland Bay in July, 1987 (R. Herbert, 1989).

The *Anthozoa* (flower-like animals) include the sea-anemones, of which the Island can boast a good selection, and corals. Nineteen species of sea-anemones have been recorded from Bembridge alone, and other good areas are

Common Starfish, *Asterias rubens,* at Ryde.

Ventnor, Hanover Point and Freshwater Bay. The Beadlet Anemone, *Actinia equina,* with a ring of bright blue beads at the base of the head of tentacles, is the commonest species. When the tide is out it contracts to a flat-topped rounded blob of jelly, usually red, but may be brown, green, yellow or, occasionally, a strawberry red with green spots, now given specific rank as *A. fragacea.* The lovely Snakelocks Anemone, *Anemonia viridis,* cannot retract its tentacles. It was not mentioned by Morey (1909) and, in fact, was first recorded at Bembridge by Miss C. Marshall in 1947. Since then it has increased enormously and is now our second most common species. Both grey and green forms will be met with. Both kinds have green algae in the tentacles, and it will be seen that they take up positions in the rock pools in full sunlight, so that the algae can make supplementary food for

mutual benefit. As in all sea-anemones, the tentacles contain sting-cells, with which prey such as shrimps are immobilised.

An Isle of Wight speciality is the Starlet Anemone, *Nematostella vectensis,* a small species with white-spotted tentacles, found in a brackish pond at Bembridge in 1935, and since found at Yarmouth (R. Herbert, 1989). Amongst other species, the handsome Dahlia Anemone, *Urticina felina,* and the Daisy Anemone, *Cereus pedunculatus,* are most likely to be seen. Compared with the corals of tropical seas, our corals are small and insignificant. One kind, however, the Soft Coral, *Alcyonium digitatum,* appropriately called Dead Men's Fingers, is often washed up with seaweeds. It consists of flesh-coloured masses of firm jelly. If placed in sea water, the outline becomes diffused by the emergence of numerous little polyps, each with eight tentacles.

The *Ctenophora*, or comb-jellies, include the Sea-gooseberry, *Pleurobrachia pileus*, which, as its name implies, is the shape and size of a gooseberry with a pair of very long branched tentacles. It may be seen from boats or piers on the surface of the sea, or in rock pools during the summer.

Still conforming to the radially symmetrical plan are the *Echinodermata* (spiny-skinned animals) comprising the starfish, sea-urchins and sea-cucumbers. Although nine species have been recorded at Bembridge (Collins *et al*, 1990), it must be admitted that these are not so commonly seen around the Island. The Common Starfish, *Asterias rubens*, has been occasionally recorded at Ryde and found off Ventnor and Bonchurch, and the common Sunstar, *Solaster papposus* is reasonably common and seen by divers in deeper water off the shore, especially in the Solent. Brittle-stars may be seen in rock pools, but are difficult to catch and identify, owing to their habit of breaking up when touched. The highest development in this class of animals was reached early in their history by sea-urchins. Although highly successful, there is no scope for any further evolutionary change, due to the restrictions imposed by their radially symmetrical plan.

An alternative to the radially symmetrical plan is that of bilateral symmetry, which is followed by the bulk of animal life. The simplest multicellular animals with bilateral symmetry are the microscopic *Rotifera*, or wheel animalcules, which are mostly found in fresh water. Its body is divided into three sections, the head, trunk and foot. The head ends in a disc bearing two rows of cilia, which are used for swimming and sweeping food particles into the funnel-shaped mouth. The movements of the cilia give the appearance of spinning wheels, hence the name. Morey (1909) contains a list of 85 species recorded in the Island by S. W. Pring and F. M. Walker, two keen microscopists, although this is only a small fraction of the 700 or so species that have been described. The *Bryozoa* (moss animals) or Polyzoa (many animals) are another group of colonial animals, commonly known as Sea-mats. Most form encrusting layers on stones or seaweeds, but some are self-supporting and form flattened, round-ended 'fronds', like some seaweeds, but sandy coloured and with a rough texture rather like 'velcro'. One of these latter called Hornwrack, *Flustra foliacea*, is frequently washed up. On close examination it will be seen to consist of many small compartments, like the cells of a honeycomb, an individual animal occupying each one. Each little animal has a U-shaped gut with a mouth surrounded by tentacles and the anus outside. The tentacles bear numerous minute vibrating cilia, which create a current of water from which the animal obtains oxygen and also collects fine particles of food which are passed to the mouth. Many different sea-mats will be found encrusting the holdfasts of the large brown seaweeds, or oarweeds. Morey (1909) listed 52 species, and recent work at Bembridge yielded 53 species, many of which were new (Collins *et al* 1990).

This brings us to the important 'Worm Pool', a mixed collection of many classes of worm-like animals. The *Platyhelminthes* (intestinal worms) include the Planarians or Flat Worms, found living free in ponds and streams as well as in the sea. If you take some bottom sediment from a pond or stream and shake it up in a glass jar and let it settle, after a time you will see Flat Worms crawling up the side of the jar, if any are present. They have a simple structure consisting of a body wall and gut, and an interesting thing about them is their power of regeneration. Any part of the body, so long as it contains a bit of body wall and gut, is capable of growing into a new individual. Some species, however, are parasitic on the higher animals, as in the case of the Liver fluke, *Fasciola hepatica*, which passes its larval stages in the marsh snail, *Lymnaea truncatula*, which is common on the Island, before infecting the liver of a sheep. Another parasitic species is the Tapeworm, *Taenia* sp., which infects man through an intermediary host such as ox or pig. No published list of Flat Worms has been compiled for the Island, although four species of Planarians have been recorded (R. Herbert, pers. comm.). The *Nematoda* are spindle-shaped unsegmented colourless roundworms, some of which are parasitic on plants and animals. They exist in every habitat, but have not been systematically

studied on the Island. The *Nemertinea* or ribbon worms occur in the sea and six species have been recorded at Bembridge (Collins *et al*, 1990), including the well named dark red Bootlace Worm, *Lineus longissimus*, in rock pools.

By far the largest phylum of worms, however, is the *Annelida*, or segmented worms, consisting of the *Polychaeta* (with many bristles or *chaetae*) found in the sea, the *Oligochaeta* (with few bristles) commonly known as earthworms, found on land, and *Hirudinea*, or leeches, found in fresh water and occasionally in the sea. Morey (1909) lists 13 species of Polychaetes for the Island, but recent work carried out at Bembridge has resulted in a total of 98 species for Bembridge alone (Collins *et al*, 1990). They are a fascinating group. Some, such as the ragworms, are free swimming, while others live in self-constructed burrows or tubes of sand or lime, from which they protrude their tentacles, which may be of so fine a texture that they display all the colours of the rainbow by refraction. In the same way as the Sea Mouse, *Aphrodite aculaeta*, looks like a lump of mud when first encountered on the beach, but if it is given a good wash in a pool of sea water, it becomes an object of exquisite beauty, as the fine hairs along its sides, which prevent the mud from entering the gills, sparkle with brilliant colours.

"Y-worm" – a Common Earthworm which has had its tail almost severed probably by a bird, and has grown a new tail, while still retaining its original one.

Typical Sea-squirts attached to seaweeds from the Solent.

The Green Ragworm, *Eulalia viridis*, is a handsome creature and one will often see its green globular egg-mass on the edge of the sea, attached to a thread, which acts as a drag-anchor, preventing the spawn from being left high and dry, or drifting out to sea, but keeping it in place in the shallow water with the full benefit of heat from the sun. No published lists have been made of earthworms or leeches in the Island, but six species of the latter have been recorded without looking too hard (R. Herbert, pers. comm.).

For my own part, I have a special affinity for earthworms. A simple description of the earthworm's structure would be: 'A tube (the gut) within a tube (the skin), with a space between containing the organs of the body.' When you come to think of it, this simple description could equally apply to ourselves and all the other animals with bilateral symmetry. It was the humble earthworm that set the pattern and made possible the development of all these forms by the process of evolution.

Not all evolution, however, is progressive. There can also be degeneration, and the best example of this is shown by the *Tunicata* or Sea Squirts. Twenty-five species have been recorded at Bembridge (Collins *et al*, 1990). The animal starts life as a larva, rather like a tadpole, with a quite distinct notochord, foreshadowing a spinal column, on the basis of which they are classified as vertebrates. When it matures, however, it degenerates and becomes sedimentary, consisting of a simple fleshy bag, with two siphons, an inlet and outlet for water, carrying food and oxygen. It is as primitive as a sponge. They are frequently attached to the bottom of boats and have to be scraped off before repainting. Colonial forms also exist as in the Golden Star Sea Squirt, *Botryllus schlosseri*, forming a flat layer of jelly with a pattern of star-shaped clusters, with coloured 'petals' round a common exhalant siphon, looking quite beautiful.

Bluebells, *Endymion non-scriptus*.

Narrow-leaved Lungwort, *Pulmonaria longifolia*, in Parkhurst.

Red Squirrel. (Photograph, Jessica Holm)

Long-eared Owl.

Plate 2 WOODLAND

Green Woodpecker.

Oak Bush-cricket, *Meconema thalassinum*.

Poplar Hawk Moth, *Laothoe populi*.

Silver-washed Fritillary.

Kestrel.

Chalkhill Blue on Carline Thistle.   Duke of Burgundy. (Photograph, Connie Pelham)

Plate 4   DOWNLAND

Adder with young.

Bee Orchid.

Great Green Bush-cricket, female.

Tufted Centaury.

Wood Calamint.

Cowslips.

Nettle-leaved Bellflower.

Plate 6   FARMLAND

Field Grasshopper, female.

Meadow Grasshopper, *Chorthippus parallelus*, female.

Barn Owl. (Photograph, Colin Fairweather)

Field Cow-wheat.

Green-winged Orchids in meadow at Jersey Camp.

Pygmy Shrew.

Field of Sunflowers.

Hedgehog.

Common Poppies.

Plate 8

MARSHES, STREAMS & PONDS

Southern Hawker.

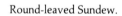

Bog Asphodel.

Large Red Damselfly.

Round-leaved Sundew.

Broad-bodied Chaser, male.

Water Vole.

Unusually coloured Common Toad.

Common Frog.

Plate 10

SALTMARSHES, ESTUARIES & RIVERS

Canada Goose and family at Newtown.

Oystercatcher at Newtown.

Little Terns and chicks at Newtown.

Ringed Plover at Newtown.

Short-winged Conehead, Male.

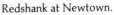

Redshank at Newtown.

Plate 12   SALTMARSHES, ESTUARIES & RIVERS

Marsh-mallow.

Common Sea-lavender.

Glasswort.

Golden Samphire.

Shrubby Sea-purslane.

(Above) Glanville Fritillary Butterfly.

(Below) Glanville Fritillary underwings.

Plate 14

CLIFFS & CHINES

Kidney Vetch.

Hoary Stock.

Red Valerian.

Wild Cabbage.

Fragrant Orchid.

Long-winged Conehead, Female.

Wall Lizard at Ventnor.

Plate 16 SEASHORE

Sun-star from the Solent.

Dog-whelks and eggs.

Shanny, *Blennius pholis*.

Limpets.

Blue-rayed Limpets. (Photograph, Roger Herbert)

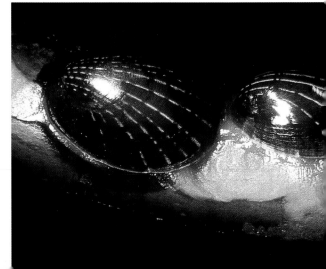

PART 2

THE HABITATS

Luccombe Chine and cliffs, with surrounding countryside
containing many habitats. (Photograph, B. Bradbury for the
National Trust).

ELEVEN

Woodlands

In order to understand fully the interdependence of wildlife in a wood, one needs to visit the same wood several times in the year, as there are so many seasonal changes. The choice of wood is also important. A deciduous wood is the most interesting, preferably a coppice with standards, even if it is not still being actively coppiced. There are many such woods in the Island, but most are privately owned and permission must naturally be obtained to visit them. Walter's Copse and Town Copse at Newtown are now open to the public, as they are owned by the National Trust, and both are rewarding. Of others open to the public, the most productive is almost certainly Parkhurst Forest, near Newport, which belongs to the Forestry Commission. Car park and picnic area are provided and there are woods of different ages and types, which can be compared. The same variety applies at Firestone Copse, near Wootton, and Combley Great Wood, near Havenstreet. Brighstone Forest, in West Wight, is a much younger forest, about the same size as Parkhurst, which is developing nicely in parts as deciduous beechwood. Borthwood Copse, owned by the National Trust, near Alverstone, contains remnants of a medieval hunting forest, while America Wood, near Shanklin, is an interesting wood in the possession of the Woodland Trust.

The effect of trees living together in a wood is to moderate all extremes of light, temperature and humidity. As soon as one enters a wood, one can feel this effect. It is nature's 'indoors', and many plants and animals benefit from these conditions. If one visits the wood early in the year, say in February or March, before the leaves appear on the trees, there is maximum light at ground level, so that mosses are at their best, and about a dozen species will be encountered. Light-

A corner of Parkhurst Forest with trees of many different ages.

demanding lichens will be found growing on the southfacing trunks of trees on the edge of the wood, or on the north side of wide rides, which have the beneficial effect of increasing the woodland edge for the benefit of wildlife. If there are beech trees present, look for the narrow pointed Door Snail, *Cochlodina laminata*, climbing up the trunk, as it feeds on the spores of lichens, algae and moss growing on the tree. It is uncannily like the bud scales shed by the beech tree at leaf burst, a good example of protective mimicry. It won't be long before the ground layer is taken over by a succession of bulbous plants – daffodil, bluebell or ramsons, in order – all racing through their life histories to flower and set seed before the leaves come out on the trees and shut out the light. It is the availability of

The Wood Spurge, *Euphorbia amygdaloides*, has evergreen leaves (top) which make food during the winter and so enable it to produce a flowering head (bottom) during the summer, when the wood is dark.

Honeysuckle, *Lonicera periclymenum,* is no friend of the forester, as, being perennial, it strangles and distorts young trees, making them suitable only for Harry Lauder walking sticks.

light, which determines what plants are able to grow and how they develop. Light inhibits growth of green plants, whereas lack of light stops growth completely. Hence the principle of forcing rhubarb. Plants, such as ferns, which continue to grow when the wood becomes dark, are able to do so because the fronds grow so big. The Wood Spurge, *Euphorbia amygdaloides*, on the other hand, has a lower part which is evergreen and able to make food during the winter to enable it to produce a flowering head in the summer in comparative darkness. Other plants use this active growth period to clamber upwards towards the light, these are the climbing plants, like Hop, Black Bryony, Clematis, Honeysuckle and Ivy.

All these plants, as well as the trees and shrubs, have fruits, which provide a store of food for the woodland mammals, such as Red Squirrel, Dormouse, Bank Vole and Wood Mouse, and birds. The Dormouse and Wood Mouse are strictly nocturnal, so are not likely to be seen, but telltale signs of their presence in the form of gnawed hazel nuts may be found. The Red Squirrel and Bank Vole are active by day, so may well be seen. Look for the Red Squirrel's nest or drey, like a round bundle of twigs in the fork of a tree five metres or more up. Both the Red Squirrel and the Dormouse spend most of their active life up in the branches of the trees, so they are comparatively safe from predators, but the Bank Vole and the Wood Mouse are prey to the carnivores, the

Treecreepers, *Certhia familiaris*, have no difficulty in finding enough insects in the wood. (Photograph, Barry Angell).

Stoat and Weasel, as well as Owls, such as the Long-eared Owl, *Asio otus*, which may be seen more likely in coniferous woods, sitting upright on a branch close to the trunk of a tree. It nests on old magpie nests or squirrel dreys in thick cover. Other woodland birds include those which nest in holes or cracks in the bark of trees, such as Blue and Great Tits, Green and Great Spotted Woodpeckers and Tree Creepers. They all feed on insects, which are plentiful in the wood, as certain trees and shrubs are the food plants of many butterfly and moth caterpillars, while many gall-wasps are intimately connected with the trees, causing the formation of numerous galls, from which more insects emerge, thus swelling the food supply. Disused woodpeckers' nests on the edge of the wood may be used by Noctule and Bechstein's Bats for roosting, which causes a distinctive stain running down the trunk from the entrance hole.

Another group of insects particularly associated with trees are those which bore into the wood, such as the Wood Wasp and species of Long-horned beetles, such as the Wasp Beetle. Some of the moths have wood-boring larvae, such as the Goat moth, *Cossus cossus*, so named because of its strong smell of goats. Adult hawk moths may well be seen resting by day on the trunks of trees, but they are hard to spot, as they are so well camouflaged. Signs of leaves being eaten will often disclose the presence of caterpillars, or segments may have been cut out and carried away by leaf-cutting bees to make their cells. You may find the pale green, ghost-like Oak Bush-cricket, *Meconema thalassinum*, on the lower branches of an oak tree, although it is usually high up in the tree. In the autumn gales it gets blown down and often enters nearby houses. The only sound it makes is by tapping the leaf with one of its hind legs in rapid short bursts. You may well become aware of a high-pitched churring noise all around you, when you are in the presence of the Wood Cricket, *Nemobius sylvestris*, which is particularly common in Parkhurst and in Borthwood. It is a hard creature to spot, as it is the same colour as the dead leaves in which it hides. On the edge of the wide rides many flowers will be attracting numerous woodland butterflies, such as the Speckled Wood, the Silverwashed Fritillary, White Admiral and Marbled White, while the ichneumon flies will be gathering to parasitise their larvae.

Pinewoods do not have anything like the variety of plants or animals associated with them, but one outstanding insect connected with them is the Wood Ant, *Formica rufa*, which is common in Parkhurst Forest and also in Firestone Copse. On the side of a ride which catches the sun for most of the day, you will see the high domed nest round the stump of a tree, made from pine needles and twigs. In Firestone Copse there are some large nests, which have existed for 60 years of more. Regular highways will be observed going out in different directions. One of these may lead to the base of a tree, up and down which you will see a constant stream of ants going up to tend their aphids and returning with a drop of honeydew. In due course, however, the trees on the other side of the ride may grow so tall that they shade the nest, which will have to be moved. Its end may well be hastened by a visit from the Green Woodpecker, which likes a meal of ants.

As autumn approaches mushrooms and toadstools of many kinds will be seen. As they do not contain chlorophyll they do not need light and obtain their energy from breaking down dead leaves and twigs shed by the trees. Together with bacteria, they make this material available to other plants in the form of rich humus. Many fungi have a special relationship with certain trees, under which they grow. It is known that close connections occur between the mycelium of the fungus and the fine rootlets of the trees, but what function they perform is not yet known. Before eating fungi one should know what species it is and what its past history is. There is no other way of telling poisonous from edible fungi. The Death Cap, *Amanita phalloides*, is found on the edge and within woods. It is absolutely deadly, and there is no known

The Deathcap, *Amanita phalloides*. Note the white gills and the volva at the base of the stem. Otherwise it is much like a mushroom, but it is deadly poisonous.

Fly Agaric, *Amanita muscaria*, with a red cap and white scales, is associated with Birch trees.

antidote, so one should learn to tell this species at once. It is like a mushroom, with a yellow or olive cap, white gills and with the base of the tem enclosed in a sheath or volva. The closely related Fly Agaric, *A. muscaria*, with a bright scarlet cap with white warts, the typical toadstool of children's picture books, is also poisonous, but not so likely to be eaten. The Panther Agaric, *A. pantherina*, looking very similar, but with a brown cap with white warts, is another poisonous species. On the other hand the violet coloured

One of many mature trees that were uprooted by the severe storm on 16th October, 1987,

Wood Blewits, *Lepista nuda*, growing in clusters on accumulations of dead leaves, is edible and delicious. Such delights are the reward for 'getting to know your fungi'. In a short time fungi will be found to be riddled with holes and crawling with thin white maggots with dark heads. These are the larvae of Fungus Midges, which will often be seen dancing in swarms close to the ground in the wood. They are, of course, quite harmless to man. Slugs also are fond of fungi, and will eat holes in the most poisonous kinds, leaving their slime trails over the cap, without any apparent ill effects. Although one must remember that, in man at least, it may be ten hours or more before the poison takes effect, by which time the slug will have gone some distance.

As winter comes on, so the trees shed their leaves and the light reaches the woodland floor once more and the moss comes into its own again. The catkins appear on the hazel trees and spring cannot be far behind.

TWELVE

Downland

'From my own experience I should have said that the best part of Freshwater Downs was near the Tennyson Monument on High Down'. So wrote J. E. Lousley (1969). He went on to say that other areas, such as Afton and Compton Downs were also highly regarded. In fact, the whole range of downs from the Needles in the west to Culver Down in the east, together with the downs round Shanklin and Ventnor, contain examples of every kind of chalkland habitat, from the sublime to the completely disastrous, according to past and present usage.. Fortunately, much of it is in the possession of the National Trust. Cer-

tainly for precious downland turf the area around Tennyson's Monument is unequalled anywhere.

Downland turf is a completely man-made and man-maintained habitat, created by cutting and clearing the native woodland for the grazing of animals, although there is some doubt as to whether this particular site was ever woodland. In order to understand the formation of such a habitat as this, one must consider the effects of three important factors: 1. Climatic, 2. Edaphic (soils) and 3. Biotic (animals and plants). The area

Tennyson's Monument on High Down, Freshwater.

is on top of south-facing chalk cliffs rising direct from the sea to a height of nearly 150m (500ft), so it receives maximum sun, mist and rain, drying winds and sea spray on some occasions. The soil consists of a thin layer of humus overlying pure chalk, except in a small area where a surface deposit of acidic clay with flints occurs. The climatic and edaphic factors are clearly not favourable for the growth of normal plants, as such rain that falls will rapidly soak through the porous chalk out of reach of the roots and drying winds and salt spray will only add to the problem. Yet, as we can see, plants in great variety do succeed in growing and forming this close-knit springy turf in spite of the bad conditions.

Originally colonisation of the bare chalk was probably by lichens and mosses, which still form a significant part of the ground flora. Mosses likely to be found and recognised include *Fissidens cristata*, with shoots like miniature fern fronds, *Ctenidium molluscum*, a yellowish-green moss of silky texture with crowded, strongly curved leaves, and *Homolothecium lutescens*, with upright stems bearing long, narrow finely pointed leaves, yellowish in colour. Towards the cliff edge, where the turf is under stress from rabbit grazing, there is a mosaic of crustose and foliose lichens, which is almost certainly the richest assemblage of chalk grassland lichens remaining in Britain, including some national rarities. Most of the species are small, but particularly notable are the sulphur-yellow patches of *Fulgensia fulgens* with orange spore-bearing bodies, and the grey-green squamules of *Squamarina cartilaginea* (C. Pope, 1986). The larvae of the rare Dew Moth, *Setina irrorella*, feed on these lichens, and the small speckled moth will be seen at dusk on Tennyson Down in June.

The most important grass is the Sheep's Fescue, *Festuca ovina*, well known for its resistance to close grazing. Many other plants, however, have adapted themselves to growing under these conditions by acquiring a long root system to obtain water from deep down in the chalk, and by growing in a rosette form, with leaves closely pressed to the ground, to conserve moisture and also to avoid drying winds and resist close grazing. Some of these plants are calcicoles, only found on the chalk, but others are quite common and widespread, but under normal conditions may grow up to two feet tall, but here they are dwarfed and only grow up to two inches high. What keeps the turf so short is the grazing of sheep and rabbits, as well as the tramp of human feet. An enthusiastic young Swede, T. Wulff, visited Freshwater in 1894 and was so intrigued by these dwarf plants that he wrote a scientific paper, published in a Swedish journal, giving new botanical names to all these dwarf forms. Needless to say these were not accepted by the authorities, and he missed the only one which was described from here as new to science, the Tufted Centaury, *Centaurium capitatum*, which has well defined differences in structure from other centauries as well as stature.

Other plants have delightful names, such as Lady's Bedstraw, Selfheal, Squinancywort, Rockrose, Clustered Bellflower, Eyebright, Salad Burnet, Marjoram and Wild Thyme. The Dwarf Thistle, *Cirsium acaulon*, is much disliked by dogs because of its rosette of prickly leaves, with a stemless flower in the centre. This, like the Carline Thistle, *Carlina vulgaris*, with its burnished bronze sepals, is a favourite source of food for the Chalk-hill Blue Butterfly, *Lysandra corydon*, which is one of many blue butterflies on the downland.

Not only are the plants small, but all kinds of life seems to be reduced in size. Small beetles, minute snails and tiny spiders are all in keeping with this miniature 'bonsai' world. The downland turf, however, is only one of several chalk grassland habitats, for, as one moves away from the sea, the effects of the climatic, and to some extent the biotic, factors are reduced, so that taller grasses, such as Upright brome, *Bromus erectus*, and Quaking-grass, *Briza media*, take a hold and dwarfing is not so pronounced. Other plants, such as Betony, *Betonica officinalis*, and many kinds of orchid are able to grow. Grasshoppers abound, filling the air with their cheerful songs. On some south-facing slopes you will see the low mounds of the Yellow Meadow Ant, *Lasius flavus*, designed to catch the maxi-

Afton Down to the east of Freshwater Bay.

mum benefit from the heat of the sun. The plant growth on these mounds is even more dwarfed by the ants employing aphids to prune their rootlets and so restrict growth. Also in their nests live very small blind white woodlice, *Platyarthrus hoffmanseggi,* which are either ignored or tolerated as useful scavengers. They are only found in ants' nests. The friable soil on the tops of the mounds is most suitable for grasshoppers to lay their eggs in. Sometimes a mound will be ravaged by a Green Woodpecker from a nearby wood.

Adders are common up on the downs, but are not often seen as they hear you coming and glide away. They feed on Field Voles, which occupy holes in the turf. They are active by day and are also hunted by Kestrels, *Falco tinnunculus,* which are frequently seen hovering over the downs, looking for signs of movement, before swooping down to catch their prey. When a vole is killed its empty nest is just what the bumble bee needs for its nest, and more bumble bees will increase the amount of pollination and ensure more viable seed for the continuation of the plant community. These are examples of the complicated interdependence of different plants and animals in the habitat. Take one away and it can have a profound effect on other forms of life.

The coarser pasture is the haunt of the Glow-

worm, *Lampyris noctiluca,* no doubt because this is the more suitable habitat for the snail, *Candidula intersecta,* and related species, on which the larva feeds. The common name is misleading as it is really a beetle, although the female does not look like one, as it has no wings. It shines its light to attract the males, which have wings and are obviously beetles. I well remember having to walk from Calbourne to my home in Brighstone one night in June and counting 17 glow-worms in a space of twenty yards alongside the road at the foot of Brighstone Down. They are not confined to the chalk, as I have several in my garden on the Lower Greensand, and the males are attracted to my porch light, with as many as seven at a time.

If sheep are replaced by cattle, other changes occur. The larger amounts of dung and urine enrich the soil and encourage the growth of large species, such as Common Ragwort, *Senecio jacobaea,* with the inevitable caterpillars of the Cinnabar moth, *Callimorpha jacobaea,* with bands of black and yellow like football jerseys. Handsome specimens of Musk Thistle, *Carduus nutans,* and Woolly Thistle, *Cirsium eriophorum,* stand out in splendid isolation, as cattle with sensitive noses steer well clear of them. They are favourite singing posts for the strident Great Green Bush Cricket, *Tettigonia viridissima*. With the enrichment of the soil there is an increase in the worm population, which in turn brings an increase in the activity of Moles, *Talpa talpa*, whose mole-hills provide areas of bare soil for the reception of seeds and consequent recruitment of more plants.

Sometimes a habitat is dominated by a particular plant. A good example is that of pasture in which the dominant plant in the spring is the Cowslip, *Primula veris*. The embankments at Carisbrooke Castle are a case in point and look quite remarkable in season. This is the food-plant of the Duke of Burgundy, *Hamaeris lucina*, a small attractive butterfly, which is not at all common. Unfortunately many good cowslip pastures have been lost through ploughing. On the edge of a small coppice on the chalk the Wood Calamint, *Calamintha sylvatica*, grows in its only British site. In spite of its name it does not seem to be a woodland plant, as it is continually trying to break out into the open and seems to prefer disturbed chalk scree. The handsome nettle-leaved Bellflower, *Campanula trachelium*, is found in the same area, as is the wild Columbine, *Aquilegia vulgaris*.

Following the arrival of myxomatosis in 1954, when the rabbit population was decimated, many areas of good downland turf turned to rough pasture, scrub and finally woodland. This is the natural succession which takes place, but for restrictions imposed by the climatic and biotic factors. I have seen the northern slopes of High Down, Freshwater, change from downland turf, through rough pasture and scrub to woodland, as it is now, in my lifetime. All is not lost, however, as the habitat changes. Indeed, one might say that there are considerable gains as new plants and animals are associated with each new habitat in turn, and we have already seen how woodland is particularly productive for wildlife. To obtain maximum benefit from chalkland, therefore, it is important to ensure that large areas of each kind of chalkland habitat are maintained by sensible management, which means the application of appropriate cutting and grazing regimes, as these biotic factors are the only ones really under our control.

THIRTEEN

Farmland

As most of the countryside is farmland, it is important to understand the effects of farming practices on wildlife of all kinds. Let us start at the beginning. About 5000 years ago the Island was virtually covered in natural deciduous forest with few open areas of marsh, cliffs and seashore. Most of the native fauna and flora, therefore, consisted of woodland species. Neolithic man first began to clear the forest to grow crops and to graze his animals, and the process was hastened by the superior tools used by Bronze Age and Iron Age people. In the Island most forest clearance occurred on the downs and in the south, but change was slow and even in medieval times the north of the Island was still largely natural woodland and a squirrel could travel from one end of the Island to the other without touching the ground. Even today our main woodland areas are found on the tertiary clays in the north of the Island.

From the 17th century there were vast improvements in agricultural practices. Grass and sheep were probably dominant in the Island, but new crops were being introduced all the time and mixed farming became a reasonable compromise. With the gradual changing pattern of the countryside the native flora and fauna was able to adapt and thrive, so that at the start of this century, with the upsurge of interest in natural history, the countryside abounded with flora and fauna of all kinds, and there was no thought of the need for conservation. It is only since 1945 that there has been any conflict between conservationists on the one hand and farmers on the other, and we must not forget that the countryside we were so fearful of losing was in fact created by the farmers themselves. The trouble was that, following the war, the increase

Typical Isle of Wight farmland around Gatcombe and Chillerton.

in population demanded an increase in the production of food at even cheaper prices, and the farming equipment available so quickened the pace of change that wildlife was no longer able to adapt. One cannot blame the farmer, as he was only responding to demand, and almost every method of increasing fertility and improving yields is harmful to wildlife. Fortunately the Island has escaped some of the worst excesses, but some damage has been done and I am not convinced that lessons have been learnt sufficiently to give one hope for the future.

One of the greatest losses has been that of permanent grass, particularly in the north of the Island, with flower-filled meadows dancing with butterflies that some of us can remember in our youth. Short-term leys of 'improved' grassland is highly productive, but quite sterile as far as wildlife is concerned. Fortunately, a few farmers still cling to the old ways, and the

Ministry of Defence at the Jersey Camp Rifle Range at Porchfield, not requiring high productivity, manage their grassland in a way to ensure that it remains as unimproved meadow used to be, loud with the song of grasshoppers and a wonderful succession of wild flowers following each other through the year. It is not open to the public, but arrangements can be made to visit, if firing is not in progress, on application to the Range Warden.

Mention has already been made in Chapter Two of the loss of cornfield weeds owing to the changes in agricultural practices and the use of herbicides. One of these is of outstanding interest. The Field Cow-wheat, *Malampyrum arvensis*, was referred to by Bromfield (1856) as having been introduced with wheat seed. It took a hold in the fields around St Lawrence and Whitwell, being partly parasitic on grasses, including wheat. It was known locally as 'Poverty Weed', because if the seed got into the wheat flour, it imparted a blue colour to the bread with such a bitter taste that it was inedible, and so made the wheat unmarketable. Farmers who had this weed on their land faced ruin and something had to be done. There were no herbicides available at that time, so the farmers, farm-workers, wives and children all set about the task of getting rid of this pernicious weed by hand-weeding the fields. They did this so successfully that today it only grows in one corner of a single field at St Lawrence, where it has been fenced off to save it from being eaten by cattle. This once pernicious weed is now a rare plant and is specially protected. It just shows what can be done without the use of chemicals, which now claim our attention.

The heightened use of chemical pesticides of all kinds has given cause for concern. Industrial chemists have worked wonders in devising chemicals to get rid of pests, but in some cases there has been a failure to understand the full effects of their products on the environment. A classic case was that of DDT and other chlorinated hydrocarbons, which undoubtedly were most effective insecticides, but, being persistent, entered the food chain with disastrous results to such predators at the end of the chain

Muck-spreader in action, putting back into the soil what has been taken out.

as peregrines and eagles. This should have been foreseen. The physicist and chemist who boasts of knowing nothing about biology, and I have met some, is a menace. Too often the wholesale application of an insecticide kills the beneficial insects and spiders that would, if left alone, deal with the pests much more efficiently than the chemical. Certainly, good advances have been made in the development of selective 'hormone weedkillers' and systemic insecticides, which have little effect on wildlife. There is an increasing interest in biological control, and organic farmers are returning to the old methods of crop rotation with some success. In spite of everything one still occasionally sees fields of golden Corn Marigold, *Chrysanthemum segetum*, particularly round Godshill, and bright scarlet Common Poppies, *Papaver rhoeas*, near Calbourne in 1988.

Before the war ponds were common features of the countryside. After 1945 many of these ponds were filled in and replaced by piped water supply to try and eliminate liver fluke in sheep. This was a great loss to wildlife. Following the severe drought in 1976, however, many farmers excavated large ponds to provide water for irrigation and incidentally attract water-fowl, so that, on balance, we are probably better off for ponds now than we were before. In addition, during the last few years, Southern Water, together with the Countryside management Service and the British Trust for Conservation Volunteers, have undertaken the clearing out and general improvement of many ponds which had become overgrown, particularly those visible from a right-of-way.

In common with other parts of the country, the removal of hedges to make larger fields to accommodate larger farm machinery has occurred in parts of the Island, as for instance south and east of Yarmouth. In some cases such hedges as were left, no longer needing to be stock-proof, were sadly neglected and became over-grown, losing their bottoms, and quite worthless for wildlife. Many parts of the Island, how-ever, remains much the same with small fields and hedges well looked after, so that we and our wildlife can be thankful. Hedges are impor-tant as extensions of the woodland edge to accommodate the largely woodland native flora and fauna. Small pockets of woodland are use-less unless they are connected to each other by hedges, which act as highways for wildlife. Small rodents, shrews and reptiles all make use of hedges, as the larger Red Squirrel also does. The well-named hedgehog often has its nest well concealed in the bottom of the hedge. Of all features hedges are probably the most beneficial to wildlife, and their replacement by barbed wire or electric fences, however convenient, is to be deplored.

Old farm buildings are not to be ignored, as swallows, barn owls and bats make use of them. Unfortunately, many of them have been separated from the farms they were originally intended to serve and have become redundant.

A well maintained pond at Upton, near Ryde.

Applications are then made to convert them into desirable residences. Admirable as some of these conversions are, they are no longer suitable for wildlife, although with luck the bats may return. Modern barns, although much more hygienic, are no satisfactory substitute, and once again it is wildlife that is the loser.

All is not lost, however, for things are rapidly changing. The formation of the Farming and Wildlife Advisory Group brought farmers and conservationists together to discuss their problems, and it was quite remarkable to what extent they agreed with each other. It has been my privilege in this connection to act as judge for the local National Farmers' Union annual Conser-vation Award, and I have invariably found that farmers and their wives have been champions of wildlife in the countryside.

FOURTEEN

Marshes, Streams and Ponds

From the wildlife point of view marshes are regarded as being particularly valuable, yet sadly diminishing, habitats. Planning authorities, by and large, fail to appreciate their value and generally regard them as derelict land suitable for draining and putting to some other use. To give maximum benefit to wildlife the marsh should be associated with the stream or pond, as they are all different stages in the wetland habitat. In order to retain the best features, it requires management, as, like the downland, there is a succession from open water, through marsh, scrub and willow carr, to woodland. All are valuable, but a variety must be aimed for, so this involves the occasional clearing out of ponds, unchoking streams, clearing of invasive sallow and so on.

The Island is fortunate in having a number of good marshes with rights-of-way running through them. A walk from Alverstone to Newchurch, particularly in June and July, is recommended. Plants of particular interest include the Nodding and Trifid Bur-marigolds, *Bidens cernua* and *B. tripartita*, the Water and Round-leaved Mints, *Mentha aquatica* and *M. rotundifolia*, common Comfrey, *Symphytum officinale*, Common Valerian, *Valeriana officinalis*, and a good display of Southern Marsh Orchids, *Dactylorchis praetermissa*. Otters, *Lutra lutra*, have been seen here in the past, but not in recent years, but one might well **hear** the 'plop' of a Water Vole, *Arvicola terrestris*, as it enters the water, and you may see where it has been grazing on the edge of the stream and has left its soft green droppings. Both Sedge and Reed Warblers, *Acrocephalus schoenobaenus* and *A. scirpaceus*, should be heard in the reed beds. This is a favourite spot for Grass Snakes, *Natrix natrix,* and

Wydcombe Pond, near Niton.

the Adder, *Vipera berus*, may be seen along the old railway track. It won't attack you, so watch it as it glides away.

In the stream you may well see shoals of Rudd, *Scardinius (Leuciscus) erythrophthalmus*, with red fins, darting hither and thither, and occasionally flash as they break surface. Damselflies are common here and it is the best place to see the striking Banded Demoiselle, *Calopteryx (Agrion) splendens*, of which the male has dark blue 'thumbprints' on its wings. The female has uniform greenish brown wings, and both sexes have emerald green metallic bodies. Other species likely to be seen are the Large Red

Damselfly, *Pyrrhosoma nymphula*, with red abdomen in the male, the Blue-tailed Damselfly, *Ischnura elegans*, with a black Abdomen with segment 8 entirely blue, and the commonest Azure Damselfly, *Coenagrion puella*, with alternate black and blue markings. Of the dragonflies, the Southern Hawker, *Aeshna cyanea*, with a striking pattern of black and green, and a little blue in the tail in the male, is the commonest, while the Common Hawker, *Aeshna juncea*, with blue replacing the green, is rather scarcer than its name suggests. Much more likely to be seen, but earlier in the year, is the Broad-bodied Chaser, *Libellula depressa*, in which the male has a powder blue abdomen, but staying yellow in the female. The Common Darter, *Sympetrum striolatum*, in which the male's adbomen turns from grey green to red, is much in evidence later in the year. Look at the herbage growing out of the water, and you may see the empty nymphal case from which a dragonfly recently emerged.

Another marsh well worth a visit is the Afton Marsh Local Nature Reserve, at Freshwater, which runs alongside the upper reaches of the Western Yar, and is a great credit to the South Wight Borough Council, who own and manage it. It has a footpath winding its way right through it, from which many interesting observations can be made. The large area of Common Reed, *Phragmites communis*, will be loud with the pulsating song of the Reed Warbler, and many familiar birds will be seen in the more wooded areas. Mallard, *Anas platyrhynchos*, will be evident in the stream. Opposite the bridge there is a favourite sandy bank where adders like to bask on a sunny day. Common Lizards, *Lacerta vivipara*, and Slow-worms, *Anguis fragilis*, are also quite likely to be seen. Once again shoals of rudd will be seen in the stream and can easily be watched for some time. Damselflies and dragonflies will be much in evidence, and the uncommon immigrant dragonflies, the Yellow-winged Darter, *Sympetrum flaveolum*, with wings of both sexes strongly suffused with saffron, and the Ruddy Darter, *S. sanguineum*, with blood red abdomen with distinct black markings, should be looked for. The Four-spotted Chaser, *Libellula quadrimaculata*, with four spots on the leading

The Lukely Brook, near Carisbrooke. (Photograph, Clive Chatters).

Common Darters mating.

edge of the forewings, has also been recorded from here.

The Island is so dominated by the chalk that acid conditions are only found in small isolated areas. Some of these are dry, but where there are wet conditions we get the specialised form of marsh known as bog. Morey (1909) considered that the Wilderness, near Chillerton, on the upper reaches of the River Medina was the best area, but drainage operations and agricultural practices

A Dragonfly Nymph.

An Emperor Dragonfly, *Anax imperator*, newly emerged from its nymphal case, which can be seen above it.

have long since completely changed the area. For a time its place was taken by old gravel workings on the top of Bleak Down to the east, but these were used for the disposal of rubbish and quite ruined. There remain a few very small isolated sites on private land, which, in spite of their isolation, manage to attract such delights as the Bog Asphodel, *Narthecium ossifragum*, and the interesting insectivorous plants such as Round-leaved Sundew, *Drosera rotundifolia*, and Pale Butterwort, *Pinguicula lusitanica*, as well as the Cross-leaved Heath, *Erica tetralix*, and several species of *Sphagnum* moss.

The trouble with ponds is that most are on private land, but if approached properly most landowners will give permission to have a closer look. Newts of all species may well be seen, as they have to rise to the surface for air at frequent intervals. One can soon learn to identify the species in the short time that they show themselves, if you follow the descriptions given in Chapter 6. There are many other forms of life which can be seen from the edge of the pond, including insects. As all adult insects breathe air, they too must come up to the surface at intervals to replenish their air supply, in the form of a bubble. The Great Silver Beetle, *Hydrophilus piceus*, which is wholly black, is our largest water beetle, second only to the Stag Beetle described in Chapter 7. It carries its bubble of air held by fine hairs on the underside of the abdomen, which gives it a silvery appearance. In spite of having a sharp spine on the underside, it is strictly vegetarian. Slightly smaller, however, is the Great Diving Beetle, *Dytiscus marginalis*, with a distinct yellow margin to its elytra (wing cases), under which the air bubble is held. This and other members of the family are fierce carnivores as larvae and adults. One will often see groups of the well-named Whirligig Beetles, *Gyrinus natator*, and other members of the same family, skimming round and round on the surface of the water. They have their eyes divided into two parts, one half looking over the surface, while the other half looks down into the water. They feed mainly on small insects that fall on the water, or occasionally dive to catch something they have seen down below.

Some water-dwelling bugs will also be seen, such as the Pond Skater, *Gerris lacustris*, which skates over the surface and also feeds on insects which fall on the water. Just under the surface one is sure to see the Water Boatman, *Notonecta glauca*, or Backswimmer, so called because it swims upside down, with eyes looking downwards on the look-out for prey. It is fiercely carnivorous. The Lesser Water Boatman, *Corixa punctata*, and related species, swim the right way up and are largely herbivorous, feeding on plant debris and algae. The diamond-shaped Water Scorpion, *Nepa cinerea*, has a long sting-like tail, which is in reality a hollow tube, which it sticks through the surface for taking in air. All these water insects mentioned have wings and are able to take flight, particularly at night, so they are well distributed. Water snails or molluscs will often be seen attached to weed, or in some cases crawling on the underside of the surface water film, which makes them easily seen. They are largely herbivorous.

The distribution maps for Frog and Toad spawning areas in Chapter 6 will give some indication of the best areas to find these engaging amphibians. They do not spend long in the water to breed in the spring, but the tadpoles may be encountered. The times when frogs and toads may be seen in ponds is variable. Records from our surveys of Frog Breeding Sites show that the earliest signs of breeding occur in the north of the Island, particularly at Northwood, near Cowes, where in most years breeding starts in January. Thereafter a wave of breeding spreads southwards, so that at Ventnor it may be March or April by the time they breed there. This is a very strange phenomenon, for which no satisfactory explanation has been given. Toads, on the other hand, may start breeding in February after a mild winter, but it is usually in the latter part of March, when most breeding occurs in communal ponds. Special road signs have been provided where numbers of toads have to cross the road in order to reach their breeding ponds, and it is hoped that this will help to reduce the horrendous slaughter of toads on the roads. Tadpoles are likely to be seen, until they emerge from the water in June or July, according to the tempera-

An effort to save toads from being run over.

ture during development. By this time the adult frogs are hard to find, but no doubt they are somewhere near in long grass, but adult toads will travel considerable distances and may be seen hunting for worms, slugs and snails after rain during the daytime and often at night. They are one of the few predators of woodlice, and they often become quite tame.

One might think that, with each female frog laying at least 1500 eggs and probably more, frogs would be much more common than they are. The answer is, of course, that they are prey to numerous animals in the pond. The Great Diving Beetle and its larvae are serious predators, as also are dragonfly nymphs, water boatmen, newts and fish. Even the adults are not immune, as they are the chief food of Grass Snakes and may well be taken by Herons, *Ardea cinerea*.

I have concentrated on all these things which are readily seen from the water's edge, but, of course, if you have the opportunity of using a pond net, you will see much more, and may well catch Three-spined or Ten-spined Sticklebacks, which are the most engaging of fish, as they make nests of duckweed roots in which the eggs are laid and the male looks after the brood until they get out of control. But, if you use a net, please take care to cause the minimum disturbance and, when you have finished, put everything back in the pond. Ponds are precious habitats and need to be respected. If, as sometimes happens, you find a Moorhen or Mallard nesting on the pond, then that is the time to pack your bags and discreetly withdraw.

Newtown Estuary from the air. (Photograph, David Motkin).

FIFTEEN

Saltmarshes, Estuaries and Rivers

Without doubt Newtown Local Nature Reserve is a classic example of a drowned estuary guarded by incurving shingle spits with extensive mudflats and saltmarshes in different stages of development. Yet I have known people who can see nothing of interest in it. To them it is a dreary landscape of mud and yet more mud, with occasional dots that others say are birds of particular kinds, but, in fact, are so far away that they are quite unrecognisable. To others, however, it is a place of enchantment. I well remember standing by a gate at the entrance to the Reserve as a school party from London came through the gate. One girl, as soon as she saw the view, stopped in her tracks and called out, 'Cor! Aint it beautiful!' It was a cry from the heart. Such an expanse of open saltmarsh, water and sky must have seemed like heaven to one brought up in London. It is beautiful and peaceful and quite unspoilt, but, more than that, it is a prime example of how the flora and fauna actually create the habitat in which they live.

A drowned estuary is caused by the river-mouth being below the high water mark of ordinary tides, so that the sea comes in and floods the estuary twice a day. At Newtown the cliffs on either side of the river-mouth are composed of tertiary sands and clays, which are being continually washed away by the sea, so that the water entering the estuary is murky with silt. In the sheltered conditions of the estuary the particles settle and form mud banks. As the tide recedes there is some scouring of the main channels, but the mud banks on the edge grow with every tide.

The first plants to colonise the mud are green algae *Enteromorpha* species, which help to increase the height. When the mud bank is

The main marsh at Newtown at high tide (top) and six hours later at low tide (bottom) showing the amount of plant life that was submerged by the tide.

sufficiently high, so that it is out of the water for more than half a day, it will be colonised by a group of plants known as halophytes, which are able to withstand being covered with sea water for varying periods. The first of these is likely to be the fleshy Glasswort, *Salicornia europaea*, sometimes called Marsh Samphire, because like the Rock Samphire, *Crithmum maritimum*, it can be picked and eaten. As the tide goes out, this will catch even more particles, so that the mud bank continues to grow until it is suitable for colonisation by the Common Cordgrass *Spartina anglica*, mentioned in Chapter 2, and it is now becoming saltmarsh. Other halophyte plants will be recruited to give further stability. Chief amongst these are the Common Saltmarsh Grass *Puccinellia maritima*, Sea Plantain, *Plantago maritima*, English Scurvygrass, *Cochlearia anglica*, so called because sailors used to eat it as a source of Vitamin C to prevent scurvy, and Annual Sea-blite, *Suaeda maritima*. Once it is firmly established, the Common Sea-lavender, *Limonium vulgare*, and Thrift, *Ameria maritima*, take over to give a splash of colour to the marsh. Many of the halophytes, such as the Glasswort and Annual Sea-blite turn a lovely red in the autumn.

Another attractive plant of the saltmarsh is the Sea Aster, *Aster tripolium*, like a small fleshy Michaelmas Daisy. The shrubby Sea-purslane, *Halimione portulacoides*, particularly likes to grow on the edges of rills, and, with its sturdy stems and roots, prevents erosion of the marsh. A feature of Newtown are the bright clumps of Golden Samphire, *Inula crithmoides*, which belong to the daisy family. Note how all the 'samphires' belong to quite different families, which make the use of common names so misleading. I hope I have explained clearly how the saltmarsh owes its existence to the very plants that grow in it. They continue to filter out particles from the very highest tides, so that for most of the time they are firm ground, on which you can walk quite safely. It is now a suitable habitat for many kinds of animals.

There is a most important molluscan fauna, including at Newtown the very small *Hydrobia ulvae*, which will be seen dotting the mud on the edge of the marsh in enormous numbers, providing a valuable source of food for birds of many kinds. There is also a small black spider of interest, *Pardosa purbeckensis*, one of the Wolf Spiders, which lives on the saltmarsh and, contrary to all the normal instincts of wolf spiders, allows itself to be covered by the sea at high tide, retaining a bubble of air, caught in hairs on its body, suffi-

cient to last until the tide goes down again. All sorts of molluscs, crustaceans and worms live in the mud of the saltmarsh and provide a valuable source of food on which the birds of the estuary depend. School Bass, *Dicentrarchus labrax*, in shoals and Grey Mullet, *Crenimugil labrosus*, of sizable proportions, will frequently be seen in the estuary, and large Common Eels, *Anguilla anguilla*, are occasionally observed, even on land.

Newtown contains the only nesting colony of the Black-headed Gull, *Larus ridibundus*, in the Island. After spasmodic nesting in 1938 and after, regular nesting started in 1958, probably as an overspill from the extensive colonies at Keyhaven and elsewhere on the mainland. They perform a most valuable service in protecting themselves, and incidentally other species, from predators like the Herring Gull *Larus argentatus*, which has also taken to nesting here, and the Carrion Crow, *Corvus corone*, from nearby woodlands. The other species deriving benefit from their protection include the Redshank, *Tringa totanus*, the Common Tern, *Sterna hirundo*, the Lapwing, *Vanellus vanellus*, and the Oyster-catcher, *Haematopus ostralegus*, which also nests on the shingle spits with the Ringed Plover, *Charadrius hiaticula*, and the Little Tern, *Sterna albifrons*, occasionally. The latter will frequently be seen diving in the pools on the saltmarsh. Shelduck nest in hedge bottoms and rabbit holes on the rising ground surrounding the estuary and bring their young down to the marsh.

Canada Geese have occasionally nested and reared their young on the marsh, but, of course, the best time to see geese is in the winter, when large flocks of Brent Geese, *Branta bernicla*, and fewer White-fronted Geese, *Anser albifrons*, fly in and take shelter in the estuary. Many species of duck do the same, with Wigeon, *Anas penelope*, and Teal, *Anas crecca*, often in large numbers, with fewer Pintail, *Anas acuta*. One of the most impressive sights at Newtown is that of large flocks of Dunlin, *Calidris alpina*, rising off the marsh and circling round, flashing white as they turn and then apparently disappearing as they merge with the background. The evocative bubbling call of the Curlew, *Nemenius arquata*, over the marshes completes the magic.

(Above) The Lapwing, *Vanellus vanellus*, nesting on the saltmarsh at Newtown.

(Right) Grey Heron, *Ardea cinerea*, with young in nest at Briddlesford Copse, Wootton. (Photograph, Colin Fairweather).

Three hides are available for birdwatchers to have a closer look. One of these is by a 'scrape' which was constructed some years ago and has been a great success. A guided Nature Trail is also available over private land, through the marsh and adjacent woodlands and meadows. For all these facilities application should be made to the Reserve Warden at the Newtown Reception Centre.

Where the marsh meets the rising land there are reeds and coarse grasses, which is the favourite habitat of numerous grasshoppers and bush-crickets, including the Lesser Marsh Grasshopper, *Chorthippus albomarginatus*, the short-winged Conehead, *Conocephalus dorsalis*, and Roesel's Bush-cricket, *Metrioptera roeselii*. Where the marsh meets the woodland of Town Copse and Walter's Copse, there are fine stands of the Marsh-mallow, *Althaea officinalis*, with its lovely velvety leaves and attractive flowers.

The features that are so well illustrated at Newtown can be seen at a number of other estuaries and inlets on the Solent shore. The estuary of the Western Yar at Yarmouth does not have such extensive saltmarshes, but the tidal water extends almost to Freshwater. It has the considerable advantage of a right-of-way along the disused railway track from Yarmouth to Freshwater, from which observations of birds of the river can be made without disturbance. There is a small area of saltmarsh at Little Thorness, to the east of Newtown, which is of interest. The Medina Estuary from Cowes to Newport also has the advantage of rights-of-way on both sides, from which good observations of interesting birds can be made. A very nice area of saltmarsh occurs at King's Quay, where the Sea-lavender already mentioned grows side by side with the Lax-flowered Sea-lavender, *Limonium humile*, so they can be easily compared. Although the Wootton Creek from Wootton to Havenstreet is a pleasant stretch of river, bordered by Firestone Copse on one side and Briddlesford Copse on the other, the estuary suffers from too much disturbance, and the impounding of the water prevents the exposure of mud at low tides for the benefit of feeding birds. Herons have their nesting site close by and will be seen here occasionally, as, indeed, they will be seen in other estuaries also.

The estuary of the Eastern Yar at Bembridge is quite different from the others, as the harbour, which used to extend up to Brading, was impounded when the railway was built. An extensive area of marsh, however, does support more birds, particularly in winter, than all the others put together. Records have been kept and published for Bird Counts at Bembridge, between September and April, from 1966 to 1983 inclusive by J. Cheverton (1972, 1978 and 1985), covering some 51 species. The last time that an Otter, *Lutra lutra*, was seen was in the river flowing through the marsh here in 1988. There is little doubt that any otters that we may have are shared with those on the rivers on the mainland, particularly the Beaulieu River, as they have been observed swimming the Solent. What is important, however, is that unpolluted access to the river through Bembridge Harbour should at all costs be maintained, and this is put in jeopardy by development plans which keep on being proposed. A number of ponds, varying in brackishness, support a good variety of damselflies and dragonflies, including the Black-tailed Skimmer, *Orthetrum cancellatum*, as well as the rare Starlet Anemone, with white-spotted tentacles, already mentioned in Chapter 10.

The Eastern Yar at Alverstone.

SIXTEEN

Cliffs and Chines

The chalk cliffs are an important feature of the Isle of Wight, extending from Compton Bay to the Needles and round to Alum Bay in the west, as well as at Culver Cliff between Sandown and Whitecliff Bay in the east and at Ventnor in the south. As one might expect not many plants take to the bare chalk, especially when it is exposed to the heat of the sun, drying winds and salt spray. Those that can survive these conditions have the added advantage that they do not suffer from competition. They are all certainly calcicoles and, in addition, have large fleshy roots to help with the conservation of moisture. On the cliffs from Compton Bay to Freshwater there are some particularly interesting plants. One of these is the Hoary Stock, *Matthiola incarna*, which is the wild plant from which the Brompton Stocks in our gardens were developed. It is quite unmistakable with large purple flowers with four petals and a most delicious scent in May and June. I remember the time when one could not see the plant as it grew on the face of the cliff, and to know it was there one had to hang one's nose over the edge of the cliff to catch its perfume. Since then, however, seeds have been blown over the cliff top, where it flowers profusely, and even to the inner cliff cut away to make way for the Military road, where a few clumps occur and can be easily photographed in comparative safety, so long as one avoids the traffic along the road.

Further along and a bit earlier in the year one will notice the yellow flowers of the Wild Cabbage, *Brassica oleracea*, belonging to the same family, *Cruciferae*, which again is the wild plant from which the many different kinds of 'greens' in our kitchen gardens were developed. When you see it growing so strongly in bare chalk, you understand why you are advised to put plenty of lime on the ground where you are growing cabbages and other 'greens', as it helps to prevent the fungal disease known as clubroot. Other yellow-flowered plants include the gorgeous Yellow Horned-poppy, *Glaucium flavum*, as well as clumps of the Kidney Vetch, *Anthyllis vulneraria*, and the Horseshoe Vetch, *Hippocrepis comosa*, and other yellow vetches which are all attractive to the blue butterflies.

At Freshwater there is yet another member of the *Cruciferae* family, the Wallflower, *Cheiranthus cheiri*, which is not a wild plant, but is more of a case where a garden plant has escaped and gone wild. It grows in cascades on the cliffs and seems to prefer the bare chalk to the pampered conditions provided by the gardener. It often grows on limestone walls, from which it gets its common name. Another handsome plant, which has escaped from cultivation is the Red Valerian, *Centranthus ruber*, which Bromfield (1856) considered to be an obvious escape only rarely found at Ventnor. Since then it has spread far and wide and has become thoroughly naturalised, growing on walls and cliffs in several parts of the Island. It is a welcome addition to our chalk flora. Another plant which has moved upwards from the cliff face, so that it is readily seen by the Military Road, is the Rock Samphire, which used to be collected for making pickle, in spite of it having a strong smell of paraffin, when crushed.

Further along the cliffs between Freshwater Bay and the Needles, there are several patches of well established plants of various kinds known as meads or greens, of which the largest is known as Rosehall Green, as mentioned in Chapter 7 as being the home of the Isle of Wight Wave moth. Here grow Rock Samphire, Sea Beet, *Beta vulgaris* subsp. maritima, pellitory-of-the-wall, *Parietaria diffusa,* Hawkweed Oxtongue, *Picris hieracioides,* and its rare parasite the Oxtongue Broomrape, *Orobanche picridis.* Apart from the Isle of Wight Wave and the Dew Moth, already mentioned in Chapter 7, a number of other interesting moths breed on the Freshwater Cliffs. These include the Beautiful Gothic, *Leucochlaena hispida,* the Feathered Brindle, *Aporophyla australis,* the Crescent Dart, *Agrotis trux,* and the Feathered Ranunculus, *Eunichtis lichenea.* A feature of the Freshwater specimens, especially the Feathered Ranuculus, is that they are unusually pale compared with specimens from elsewhere. This would seem to be a clear case of evolutionary change due to natural selection in favour of those which are most inconspicuous on the chalk cliff.

The cliffs of Main Bench towards the Needles become more vertical and are not able to support much in the way of plant life. But they do have distinctive horizontal ledges, which are made use of by the Guillemots and Razorbills mentioned in Chapter 5. They do not build nests, but lay a single egg on this narrow ledge, however precarious it may seem. The Cormorants, on the other hand, build quite substantial nests of seaweeds, and will often be seen with their white collars, holding their wings out to dry after a spell of fishing under water, thus earning its local name of Isle of Wight Parson.

The cliffs from Compton Bay to the east are composed of soft sands and clays, which are easily eroded and slump towards the sea, forming miniature undercliffs. The vegetation on these slumping cliffs is quite different from that on the cliff top, which in the main is cultivated ground. On the cliff it is largely dominated by such plants as Great Horsetail, Coltsfoot, *Tussilago farfara,* and Common Reed, *Phragmites communis,* which are able to survive the constant erosion by having numerous underground stems, or rhizomes. This is the favourite site for the Glanville Fritillary butterfly, whose caterpillars feed on the young ribwort plantain plants, which colonise the bare soil constantly being exposed by erosion. A wealth of other plants are able to gain a hold, at least for a short time, so that the undercliffs are ideal landing grounds for migrant butterflies such as the Clouded Yellow, which in

good years may be seen in large numbers. In the slumping cliffs small ponds are formed, in which large numbers of toads breed each year, in spite of being so near to the sea. All three species of British newts also breed in these ponds, as well as a colony of African Clawed Toads, which were released in one of the ponds in 1967, since when they have bred regularly, as mentioned in Chapter 6.

Further east, between Atherfield Point and St Catherine's, there are a number of 'chines', which is a local name for a ravine, or deep narrow gorge. They can be seen in various stages of development. They are originally formed by a small stream cutting its way through the soft sandy strata, so making the initial cleft. After this the prevailing south-west wind blows up the cleft and blasts the sides of the chine, as can be shown by the extensive dunes of blown sand which exist on the cliff top to the east of the chine.

Whale Chine is undoubtedly the most impressive of these chines and well worth a visit. Access is made easy by the provision of a series of well maintained steps, but it must be stressed that bathing is prohibited, however tempting, as there is a most dangerous under-tow in certain states of the tide. At the bottom of the chine there is an area of undercliff, completely isolated by the sheer cliff face on the inland side and the sea on the other. In spite of this isolation, or perhaps because of it, there is a unique assemblage of wildlife to be found here. The dominant plant is the Common Reed. Once again in the evening the undercliff becomes alive with Common Toads, which breed in the small ponds. They must be regularly sprayed with salt water, but they clearly do well here. An uncommon dragonfly, the Keeled Skimmer, *Orthetrum coerulescens,* also breeds in these ponds and nowhere else in the Island. The banks of freshly fallen sand at the foot of the cliff are a favourite site for the Green Tiger Beetle, *Cicendela campestris,* and the much rarer Brown Tiger Beetle, *C. germanica,* is also found here, but nowhere else in the Island. It was here, too, that Dr Blair found a bush-cricket new to Britain in 1931. This was the long-winged Conehead, *Conocephalus discolor,* and for a long time this was the only known site

in Britain, until it was discovered in similar situations in Sussex and Dorset in the late 1940's. Another interesting creature found here is the Ant-mimic Spider, *Myrmarachne formicaria*, which raises its front legs to simulate antennae and runs about on its other three pairs of legs just like an ant. It has also been found in Parkhurst Forest, which would be much more appropriate as it strongly resembles a Wood Ant.

Each chine is different, and each has its own specialities. Luccombe Chine is well-wooded and most attractive. At the bottom there is an undercliff, here the Marsh Hellebrorine, *Epipactis palustris*, can be seen. Shanklin Chine is also well-wooded, and has a superb waterfall, which keeps the atmosphere constantly damp, so that it is a particularly good place for liverworts, mosses and ferns.

The Undercliff from Niton to Luccombe is a special area with an imposing inner cliff of Upper Greensand topped with Chalk. The Undercliff itself is a tumble of rocks and soils of different kinds, suporting a most varied flora and fauna encouraged by the southerly aspect and sheltered conditions. This can best be shown by a visit to

Whale Chine, near Chale. (Photograph, David Motkin).

Oxtongue Broomrape, *Orobanche picridis*.

The Undercliff at St. Lawrence. (Photograph, David Motkin).

the Ventnor Botanic Gardens at Steephill, where exotic plants of many kinds are able to grow and survive in the open. The European Wall Lizard may be seen in gardens and on the cliffs in Ventnor. The slopes of Bonchurch Down are completely covered with Evergreen Oak, *Quercus ilex,* due to two brothers in the last century, who filled their pockets with acorns and planted them at intervals whenever they went for a walk. It is a mixed blessing, however, as the trees tend to spread to adjoining precious downland, but it is a unique habitat, which may well produce some interesting surprises in the future. A word of warning – the dead leaves of the Evergreen Oak on the steep slope are dangerously slippery, so take care.

The cliffs on the north coast of the Island are also very much subject to erosion, but are not sufficiently high to produce useful undercliffs. There is considerable slumping, however, and one common feature that one should be aware of is the 'mud-glacier', which can be encountered in a number of places. It is a stream of semi-liquid mud moving slowly down the cliff face to the shore. They are easily recognised for most of the time, but in the summer a thin crust of dry and cracked mud will form on the surface, giving the appearance of firm solid ground. Many a visitor has been taken in by this, and has jumped on to what was thought to be solid ground, only to go through into yellow liquid mud up to the thighs. Be warned and watch your step. Once again the dominant vegetation is Great Horsetail, but here and there there are wonderful displays of orchids, such as Common Spotted-orchids and Green-winged Orchids. The slumping cliffs below Headon Warren close to Totland Bay are particularly good for the lovely Fragrant Orchid, *Gymnadenia conopsea,* with its delightful scent of cloves, and the Marsh Helleborine growing together and in considerable numbers. But please remember the rule – they must not be picked.

SEVENTEEN

The Seashore

Catastrophes can and do happen occasionally in any habitat. For instance, in October 1987, the great storm played havoc with many of our woodlands; precious downland turf may be ploughed up; hedges may be removed; ponds and streams may dry up, as in the serious drought of 1976; serious cliff falls may occur; but, in general, the habitats we have considered so far are fairly stable and such changes as do occur tend to be gradual, so that plants and animals are well able to adapt to the changing conditions.

When it comes to the seashore, however, we have a major catastrophe occurring, not once, but twice a day, as the tide goes out and leaves the plants and animals high and dry, deprived of the water upon which they depend. One might well wonder why, under such circumstances, there is any life on the seashore at all, but the answer would appear to be that, so far as plants are concerned, the need for light as a source of energy for making food and minerals takes precedence over anything else. Apart from the plankton in the surface waters of the sea, marine plants are virtually restricted to that narrow belt of shallow water on the edge of the sea, that we know as the seashore. As primary producers of food, it follows that they will attract the primary consumers amongst the animals, and they in turn will attract the secondary consumers, or predators, and so the habitat becomes populated.

Not every shore, however, is equally favourable for plants and animals. The shingle beach, composed of rounded pebbles constantly turned over by the sea, as in the centre of Freshwater Bay and along the coast at the foot of Whale Chine, is too unstable to support any plant life or animal life. The sandy beaches at Ryde, Sandown and Compton Bay seem at first to be devoid of life, as no plants can gain a hold on the shifting sands, but, in fact, there is a wide variety of animals living in the sand. Worms of many species are numerous, some living in tubes or burrows, while others move freely through the damp sand. It is the ideal home for such burrowing molluscs as the razor shells. There is no sharp division between the sandy and the muddy shore, but one intergrades with the other according to the amount of organic debris present. The best muddy shores are on the north coast bordering the Solent. Once again, they are populated with large numbers of worms, particularly the Lugworm and tubeworms of various kinds, as well as molluscs that form surface burrows such as the Edible Cockle, and those that form deeper permanent burrows like the Blunt Gaper, *Mya truncata*. Occasionally rocks and shingle banks may support some seaweeds, as well as Oysters and Mussels, which often bind themselves together with byssus threads to avoid being washed away. Similarly the inevitable Slipper Limpets join together to form long chains. Rocky shores, such as those at Bembridge, Culver, Bonchurch, Hanover Point and Freshwater Bay, are by far the most productive as, being more stable, they support a wide range of seaweeds, which provide food and shelter for an equally wide range of animals.

When studying life on the seashore, it is important to know and understand the effects of the tides. These are caused by the gravitational pull of the sun and the moon on the oceans. At both full and new moon the sun and moon are in line with the earth, so that their combined effect causes 'spring tides', which come high up the beaches and also go a long way down. For seven days after spring tides the angle between the sun

Thong Weed, *Himanthalia elongata*, is very tough.

Common Whelk, *Buccinum undatum*, with sponge-like egg capsules, from which very few young whelks emerge, as they eat each other.

and the moon increases, so that their combined effect decreases and we have 'neap tides', when the water movement is much reduced. Overlying this monthly rhythm of tides is an annual rythm, when the spring tides get progressively larger as the equinoxes approach when the periods of daylight and darkness are equal, on 21st March and 21st September. These are the highest and lowest tides of the year.

The shore may be conveniently divided into zones, according to these tidal movements. The Middle Shore is an extensive region bounded above the average high tide level and below by the average low tide level. In the main, therefore, it experiences twice daily submergence under the sea followed by exposure to the air, which are typical shore conditions, to which the bulk of plants and animals are adapted. The Lower Shore is the narrow region extending from the average low tide level to the limit of extreme low water springs. It is only uncovered when the tides exceed the average range. The Upper Shore, on the other hand, is continually exposed, except when the tides exceed the average range. There are also two recognised marginal zones, the Sub-littoral Zone just below the extreme low water springs, which is never uncovered, but supports a variety of small red seaweeds and large brown seaweeds, such as Oar Weeds,, Thong-weed, *Himanthalia elongata*, and Sea Bootlace, *Chorda*

filum, which can be dangerous to those who dive off boats. Above the Upper Shore there is the Splash Zone, which is never covered by the tide, but receives splashes at high water springs, especially when the upper shore is rocky. Seaweeds tend to give way to lichens, which are best seen at St Catherine's Point.

It is of considerable interest that in the Island high water springs is at noon and midnight, Greenwich mean Time, so that the lower shore is only exposed around 06.00hrs and 18.00hrs, and are therefore not put at risk by exposure to the heat of the midday sun. In addition to this, the central position of the Island along the south coast ensures that a tidal surge through the Straits of Dover and down the Channel reaches the Island just as the tide is beginning to go out. This gives rise to the so-called double tides of the Solent, when there is a two-hour stand at high tide, thus reducing the time that the shore is exposed. This phenomenon is, of course, of inestimable benefit to Southampton as a major port, and to yachtsmen and holidaymakers in general, by increasing the time of high tide, but for those of us bent on studying seashore life time is correspondingly shorter. For this reason, it is best to follow the tide out, and make sure that one does not get cut off, when the tide returns.

Although everything looks calm and peaceful when the tide is out, one must realise the

Acorn Barnacles, *Balanus balanoides*, at Bembridge.

traumatic effects that losing their water is having on the plants and animal on the shore. The hazards of the shore are considerable and include the risk of desiccation by drying winds, overheating from the sun in summer and cold from frost in winter, dilution by rain and buffeting by waves as the tide comes in again, not to mention severe storms at certain times of the year.

Taking the seaweeds first, it is a general rule that a particular weed will grow as high up the beach as it can, to obtain maximum light, consistent with its ability to withstand desiccation. They do not have roots, but are attached to a firm substrate, such as rocks, by holdfasts and take in what they require directly from the surrounding water. They reproduce by spores, although they may have a sexual generation, producing sperm and eggs in the course of their life cycle. The brown seaweeds are tough and leathery and predominate on the middle shore, while green seaweeds are more likely to be seen on the upper shore, particularly where fresh water is draining from the land. Red seaweeds, which are usually much smaller, are commonest on the lower shore and in rock pools. The Eel Grass, *Zostra* sp., is a flowering plant with roots, leaves and flowers, which grows in sandy areas on the lower shore. There are three species round

the Island, and they are an important food source for Brent Geese in winter. By lying flat on the shore, when the tide is out, the brown seaweeds help to conserve moisture, and many animals will be found taking advantage of this damp environment, but, when the tide comes in, they rise in the water either by having gas-filled bladders or by having their substance lighter than seawater. This creates a virtual forest of growth, which provides much needed shelter for animals from their enemies. In order to withstand the buffeting by the waves as the tide comes in, the animals of the shore adopt one or other of a number of strategies and are most easily recognised as being 'stickers, rollers or hiders'.

The most obvious 'stickers' are the Common Barnacles firmly attached to the rocks. They look quite lifeless when the tide is out, but when it comes in they open their trap-doors and frantically sweep their feathery legs through the water to catch small particles of food brought in by the tide. Some serpulid worms with limy tubes are permanently fixed to rocks, shells and seaweeds, while many other animals like sponges, hydroids, moss animals and compound sea-squirts are firmly attached to rocks and seaweeds, so they must be regarded as successful 'stickers'. The Common Limpet is firmly fixed when the tide is out, but when the tide comes in it lifts its shell and moves around feeding on small plantlets, returning to exactly the same spot, where its shell fits the rock and makes a water-tight seal, as the tide goes out again. This is why there is

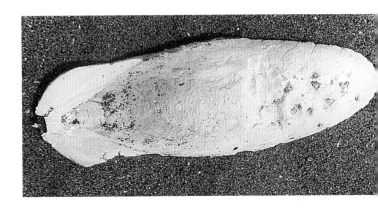

Cuttlefish "bone", which has been pecked by birds to obtain lime to make their eggshells.

125

always a bare patch on the rock where limpets are seen. The Chiton or Coat-of-mail Shell is another temporary 'sticker'. Even some fish, like the Lumpsucker, *Cyclopterus lumpus*, and others have their pelvic fins adapted as suckers, by which they cling to the rocks.

The most obvious 'rollers' are the molluscs with a single strong rounded shell, like the Dog Whelk, periwinkles and top shells. The first wave that hits them will inevitably knock them off the rock or seaweed, and they will suffer themselves to be rolled about, until the calmer water will allow them to regain their position. Likewise, the Hermit Crab, using a discarded shell, is able to withdraw right into the shell, so that it avoids damage as it is rolled about.

Many animals are 'hiders', taking advantage of crevices in the rocks, or burrowing in sand or mud or under rocks to escape the effects of the turbulent waters. Crabs and other crustaceans, like shrimps and prawns, as well as echinoderms, including starfish and sea urchins, are all good 'hiders'. There is no more successful 'hider' than the Common Piddock that bores into the rock as it grows, so that it can never escape, but is safe in the rock, as least until the rock itself is worn away.

The study of life in the rock pools brings the greatest reward, for here we can see at close quarters many of the plants and animals whose natural home is in shallow offshore waters. We are privileged indeed to be allowed to enter this fascinating world of the seashore. It behoves us, however, to take the greatest care and cause the least disturbance possible to the inhabitants. It is their world, and, as we have seen, they have natural hazards enough without our adding to them.

PART 3

CONSERVATION

St. Catherine's Down and Hoy Monument. (Photograph,
Roger Smith for the National Trust).

EIGHTEEN

Conservation on the Island

My predecessor as author of a book bearing the same title as my own, Frank Morey (1909), marvelled in his introduction at the infinite variety which is displayed in objects both animate and inanimate, and the constant change which was taking place in everything around him, whether it be apparent or not. He was an inveterate collector and amassed in the course of his life a collection of local natural history objects, including between 2000 and 3000 species of insects, shells and plants with, in most cases, data as to habitats and localities, where they were found. These undoubtedly were of great value to him in the compilation of lists of species that were in important feature of his book. He made no apologies for the destruction of life that this entailed, but used persuasive arguments to justify the collection of specimens.

He records how a large heap of garden refuse, which had been accumulating in his garden for several months, was about to be burnt. He took a bucketful of this material and counted the several hundred insects, spiders, woodlice, centipedes and worms that it contained, and worked out that there must be 30,000 to 40,000 individuals which were about to be destroyed in the fire. If we are justified, he argued, in destroying so many lives for the trifling convenience of ridding ourselves of a heap of garden refuse, how much more justified should we be in filling our cabinets with a well selected series of specimens which would afford material for study for a lifetime and would be enough to illustrate very fairly the insect fauna of a whole county.

This is a false argument, as the acceptance of one does not necessarily imply acceptance of the other for, if it did, nature would be the double loser. One must admit, however, that for these pioneer naturalists there was a need to collect specimens to describe, illustrate and identify their finds with accuracy, resulting in the remarkable books that were an invaluable product of the Victorian age for the benefit of future naturalists.

There was no thought of conservation at that time, as everything was so prolific, with meadows rich with wild flowers and butterflies in their hundreds by the wayside. Nature was so bountiful that the idea of any species becoming extinct was unthinkable. In fact, when he founded the Isle of Wight Natural History Society in 1919, there was still no mention of conservation in the rules of the Society. It was not until 1960, when I was President of the Society, that the rules were rewritten and one of the objects was declared to be, 'To promote in every way possible the conservation of the flora and fauna of the Isle of Wight, and the proper preservation of all objects of special archaeological and geological interest.' S. T. Waite was appointed as the first Conservation Officer and a Conservation Committee was formed. Since then it has become a matter of increasing importance both locally and nationally.

So far as legislation is concerned, those interested in birds were the first in the field. Even before the Society for the Protection of Birds (now the R.S.P.B.) was formed in 1889, the Seabirds Protection Act of 1869, which was of special interest to the Isle of Wight, gave legal protection during the breeding season to all our usual seabirds (except Cormorant and Shag), which had previously been shamelessly persecuted, not only by egg and feather collectors, but regrettably by outstanding naturalists of the day, such as Edward Newman, the Editor of *The Zoologist*, and his shooting friends. This was

Slumping Cliffs by Headon Warren, near Totland. (Photograph, Brian Bradbury for the National Trust).

superseded by the Wild Birds Protection Act of 1880, protecting all birds (including young, but not eggs) during the breeding season, although authorised persons, usually landowners, could take birds not specially scheduled. This was reinforced by the 1894 Act, which empowered county councils to apply for an order to prohibit the taking or destroying of birds eggs in any year or in any place within that county. The Isle of Wight, which had only been made a separate administrative county in 1890, made such an order in 1896 relating to Culver Cliffs and the cliffs at Freshwater and Totland. There then followed a sequence of similar Orders, made by the Secretary of State on application by the County Council, until the Protection of Birds Act

1954, which gave protection to all birds and their eggs, unless they were specifically excluded. It also established Statutory Bird Sanctuaries in those areas where previous legislation had applied, but the County Council of the time, in spite of having been so diligent in applying for orders during the previous 60 years, failed to recognise their existence and apparently lost all interest. One important result of this legislation, however, was that, with the support of teachers in schools, it virtually put a stop to the habit of collecting eggs by small boys and completely changed the attitude of a generation. The Protection of Birds Act 1967 gave further protection to birds by making it an offence to disturb certain birds at their nests, a measure that became necessary with the increasing popularity of bird-watching and photography.

When one considers that it had taken 100 years to formulate legislation for the protection of birds, it is remarkable how much progress has been made in dealing with the larger question of protection for wildlife and the countryside in general. The National Trust had been formed in 1895 'to act for the nation in the acquisition of land and houses worthy of permanent preservation'. The public are given free access to the Trust's open spaces, subject to the requirements of farming, forestry and the protection of nature. Though 'national' in name and function, the Trust is independent of the State, and is *not* a Government department. In the Island, apart from Bembridge Windmill and the Mottistone estate, the Trust has concentrated on the purchase of land and owns important stretches of downland, coastal cliffs, moorland and woodland, as well as the Newtown Estuary forming the Newtown Local Nature Reserve. There is no better protection of these areas than to be in the possession of the National Trust.

The concept of Nature Conservation arose in the dark days of the Second World War, when a few dedicated individuals prepared reports and made recommendations to Government. As a result the Nature Conservancy was created by Royal Charter in 1949 and in the same year the National Parks and Access to the Countryside Ace 1949 was passed. The Nature Conservancy was constituted 'to provide scientific advice on the conservation and control of the natural flora and fauna of Great Britain; to establish, maintain and manage nature reserves in Great Britain, including the maintenance of physical features of scientific interest; and to organize and develop the scientific services related thereto'. There were no national nature reserves in the Island, but a number of Sites of Special Scientific Interest (S.S.S.I's) were scheduled in 1951. These have been reviewed at regular intervals and others added, so that there are 38 such sites at the present time. Considerable help was also given to the setting up and management of the Newtown Local Nature Reserve by the County Council in 1966.

Under the 1949 Act a number of National Parks were established by agreements with landowners and the National Parks Commission (NPC). Local Authorities were also required to prepare definitive maps showing public rights-of-way. In 1965 the NPC was replaced by the Countryside Commission and a large part of the Island was declared an Area of Outstanding Natural Beauty (AONB) with some protection from undesirable development.

The most important Wildlife and Access to the Countryside Act 1981 built on the foundations of the 1949 Act, but considerably extended the protective measures to cover a whole range of plants and animals, some of which, like bats, received total protection. So the position is that there is no shortage of legislation, and it only requires the will of all concerned to put it into operation.

There are serious gaps, however, to which attention should be paid as soon as possible. As an example, the Badger is fully protected, but its sett can be filled in or bulldozed to extinction with impunity. The situation with regard to fossil collecting is quite extraordinary. The old maxim of 'finder's keepers' seems to apply, without any regard to the rights of the landowner from whose land the fossil has been taken. This is of the utmost importance in the Island, as there is a Museum of Isle of Wight Geology at Sandown, which would benefit greatly from the scientific assessment of such fossils in their proper context and make them available for viewing by the public. Instead of which visitors take off the fossils, which are valueless without the precise details of location and horizon in which they were found, and no doubt are eventually thrown away. Even more serious is the practice of parties from the Continent, where the taking of fossils is strictly controlled, coming over to the Isle of Wight with their heavy equipment to take advantage of our lax laws for purely commercial gain. It should be stopped and soon, if we are to retain anything of our heritage.

The collecting habit dies hard. The collection of discarded seashells does little harm, except to perpetuate the habit of collecting. Why is it that people have to be so possessive, when the living plants and animals are all around them to be seen and enjoyed at one's will? The birdwatchers have put their house in order, and others should follow their example. The sale of bird's eggs has been made illegal, but unfortunately there is still some illicit trade carried on, which necessitates the RSPB to employ numerous wardens to maintain a 24-hour watch on the Osprey's nests in Scotland. In the case of butterflies, there is considerable trade in live specimens of rare species from this country as well as abroad, which appears to be still legal. In some cases this can be beneficial, if they are bred free from their parasites and released in their appropriate habitats, but more often they are bred to obtain slight aberrations as an excuse to amass large collections again.

The collecting and picking of flowers is not nearly so common as it used to be. With the development of cheap colour film, people seem to be happy to collect photographs of their finds, which is all to the good. The camera has in many cases replaced the gun, but the laws relating to shooting, although recently tightened, leave much to be desired. It seems quite wrong that shooting rights can be retained by an agent, when selling land. Such a case occurred when the Newtown Estuary was sold to the National Trust and later declared as a Local Nature Reserve by the County Council. This gave rise to the anomalous situation whereby public money was being spent to ensure the conservation of birds in the estuary, only to have them shot out of the sky by the syndicate who retained the shooting rights, although, in fairness, it must be said that they did not often claim their rights. There would be no such conflict, if shooting rights by law were always vested in the owner of the land.

There are many organisations now involved with conservation in the Island. Apart from the Isle of Wight Natural History and Archaeological Society already mentioned, there is the Hampshire and Isle of Wight Naturalists' Trust Ltd., one of many county trusts under the auspices of the Royal Society for Nature Conservation (RSNC), the Council for the Protection of Rural England (CPRE), the Solent Protection Society (SPS), the Farming and Wildlife Advisory Group (FWAG), the Isle of Wight Society (IWS) and the Friends of the Earth (FoE). All are dedicated to the cause of conservation and are worthy of support. Some regret that there are so many organisations involved and feel that it would be better if there was one large organisation able to speak with one voice, but I feel that there is room for them all, as nature conservation is such a complicated issue that needs a number of different points of view to be expressed. Providing they work together and not against each other, they have the best chance of reaching a satisfactory conclusion.

What are the threats, and where do they come from? We have already seen the natural hazards, such as serious frost, drought and violent storms, which can cause havoc enough in the countryside; but the real threats to the continuation of the Island as a microcosm of south-east England are in the proposed developments of many kinds in the interest of so-called tourism. For the last 100 years the island has benefited from visitors, who have been captivated by its natural charms. Once captivated they have returned again and again, while the residents have had much to be thankful for. In recent years, however, there have been grandiose schemes proposed, which, if carried out, would attract quite a different kind of visitor, to whom the world of nature would mean nothing. The implementation of such schemes would inevitably incur the loss of valuable countryside. Woods, downland, farmland, marshes, saltmarshes, would all be at risk. Such schemes would no doubt make a handsome profit for the promoter, but for the Island it would be disastrous. The whole trend of today, with even larger ferries, more cars on the already over-used roads, more houses packed close together, are likely to destroy the peace and quiet of the Island for ever.

The natural resources of our wonderful Island, as only partly revealed in this book, must be preserved at all costs, for this is our Heritage, for which we should be forever grateful and pass on intact to future generations.

Useful Addresses

Readers of this book may well wish to seek for further information or contribute their own records. The Isle of Wight Natural History and Archaeological Society appoint local Recorders for this purpose. The following is the current list of Recorders:

Birds – John Stafford, Westering, Moor Lane, Brighstone, I.W. PO30 4DL.

Botany and Beetles – Bill Shepard, 87 Elm Grove, Newport, I.W. PO30 1RN.

Bryophytes – Mrs Lorna Snow, Ein Shemer, Upper Hyde Farm Road, Shanklin, I.W. PO37 7PS.

Butterflies – Barry Angell, Downsview, Locksgreen, Porchfield, I.W. PO30 4PE.

Conservation and Lichens – Dr Colin Pope, 13 Bedworth Place, Ryde, I.W. PO33 2RF.

Geology, Steve Hutt, Museum of Isle of Wight Geology, County Library, High Street, Sandown, I.W. PO36 8AF.

Hemiptera and Galls – Dr David Biggs, Plum Tree Cottage, 76 Albert Road, Gurnard, Cowes, I.W. PO31 8JU.

Mammals, Reptiles, Amphibians and Orthoptera – Oliver Frazer, Mottistone Mill, Brighstone, I.W. PO30 4AW.

Marine Life – Roger Herbert, 20 Chapel Street, Newport, I.W. PO30 1PY.

Molluscs – Dr Richard Preece, Firethorn Cottage, 2 Comberton Road, Toft, Cambridge.

Moths – Peter Cramp, Stone Cross Cottage, Godshill, I.W. PO38 3HZ.

Myriapods, etc – Andy Keay, 46 Albany Road, Newport, I.W. PO30 5JA.

It will be appreciated that these names and addresses may change over the years. If there is any difficulty in making contact, readers are advised to write to the Secretary of the Society, who will forward the letter on to the appropriate person. The current Secretary is: Mrs Toni Goodley, Ivy Cottage, New Barn Lane, Shorewell, I.W. PO30 3JQ.

In the event of a change in secretary, the latest edition of Whitaker's Almanack should be consulted.

Other useful addresses are:

Hampshire and Isle of Wight Naturalists' Trust Ltd, 71 The Hundred, Romsey, Hampshire SO51 8BZ.

National Trust (I.W.), 35a St James' Steet, Newport, I.W. PO30 1LB.

Nature Conservancy Council, Regional Office, Foxhold House, Thornford Road, Crookham Common, Newbury, Berks RG15 8EL. (Local Office – 1 Southampton Road, Lyndhurst, Hants).

Bibliography

Adams, D. 1856. *History of the Isle of Wight*. London.

Adams, L. E. 1892-1933. Personal Nature Diaries (unpublished).

Alexander, J. 1964. Report on the Excavation of a Round Barrow on Arreton Down, Isle Wight. *Proc. Isle of Wight nat. Hist. archaeol. Soc.* (for 1962). 5(7): 288-309.

Alexander, K., Goodenough, S. & Pope, C.R. 1990. The Storm of 16th October, 1987. *Proc. Isle Wight nat. Hist. archaeol. Soc.* (for 1989). 9:161-166.

Bevis, J., Kettell, R. & Shepard, B. 1978. *Flora of the Isle of Wight*. Yelf Bros.

Biggs, D. T. 1979. *Andricus quercus-calicis* – a New Gall on the Island. *Proc. Isle Wight nat. Hist. archaeol. Soc.* (for 1976). 7(1): 45-46.

Biggs, D. T. 1989. Additional Records of Plant Galls on the Isle of Wight. *Proc. Isle Wight nat. Hist. archaeol. Soc.* (for 1988). 8(3): 12-13.

Biggs, D. T. 1989. Additional Records of Plant Galls in the Isle of Wight. *Proc. Isle Wight nat. Hist. archaeol. Soc.* (for 1989). 9: 5-7.

Blair, K. G. 1951. *Neuroptera* of the Isle of Wight. *Proc. Isle Wight nat. Hist. archaeol. Soc.* (for 1950). 4(5): 157-162.

Blair, K. G. 1952. The Wainscots of Freshwater Marsh. *Proc. Isle Wight nat. Hist. archaeol. Soc.* (for 1951). 4(6): 205-212.

Blair, K. G. 1953. A Supplementary List of *Coleoptera* of the Isle of Wight. *Proc. Isle Wight nat. Hist. archaeol. Soc.* (for 1952). 4(7): 263-267.

Bonner, L. H. 1984. Management of Countryside Recreation – a Case Study in the Isle of Wight. *Proc. Isle Wight nat. Hist. archaeol. Soc.* (for 1982). 7(7): 489-496.

Brightman, F. H. & Nicholson, B. E. 1966. *The Oxford Book of Flowerless Plants*. O.U.P.

Bromfield, W. A. 1856. *Flora Vectensis*. W Pamplin.

Brough, P., Gibbons, B. & Pope, C. 1986. *The Nature of Hampshire and the Isle of Wight*. Barracuda Books.

Burland, C. B. 1976. A Survey of the Red Squirrels of the Isle of Wight. *Proc. Isle Wight nat. Hist. archaeol. Soc.* (for 1975). 6(10): 642-646.

Burr, M. 1909. List of *Othoptera* in Morey's *Guide to the Natural History of the Isle of Wight*. Isle of Wight County Press.

Bury, C. A. 1844-1845. Notes on the Birds of the Isle of Wight in *The Zoologist 2 & 3*. London.

Butler, E. A. 1909. List of *Hemiptera* in Morey's *Guide to the Natural History of the Isle of Wight*. Isle of Wight County Press.

Cheverton, J. M. 1972. Bird Counts at Bembridge, 1966-1972. *Proc. Isle Wight nat. Hist. archaeol. Soc.* (for 1971). 6(6): 448-456.

Cheverton, J. M. 1978. Bird Counts at Bembridge, 1972-77. *Proc. Isle Wight nat. Hist. archaeol. Soc.* (for 1977). 7(2): 91-99.

Cheverton, J. M. 1985. Bird Counts at Bembridge – 3. *Proc. Isle Wight nat. Hist. archaeol. Soc.* (for 1983). 7(8): 616-624.

Cheverton, J. M. 1988. *Odonata* of the Isle of Wight. *Proc. Isle Wight nat. Hist. archaeol. Soc.* (for 1987). 8(2): 29-32.

Cheverton, J. M. 1989. *Breeding Birds of the Isle of Wight*. Isle of Wight County Press.

Cheverton, J. M. & Pelham, C. N. 1989. Current Status of Isle of Wight Moths. *Proc. Isle Wight nat. Hist. archaeol. Soc.* (for 1988). 8(3): 22-36.

Cheverton, J. M. & Shepard, B. 1987. *Watching Birds in the Isle of Wight*. Isle of Wight County Press.

Clifford, M. H. 1937. A Mesolithic Flora in the Isle of Wight. *Proc. Isle Wight nat. Hist. archaeol. Soc.* (for 1936). 2(7): 582-594.

Cohen, E. & Taverner, J. 1972. *A Revised List of Hampshire and Isle of Wight Birds*.

Colenutt, G. W. 1909. An Outline of the Geology of the Isle of Wight in Morey's *Guide to the Natural History of the Isle of Wight*. Isle of Wight County Press.

Colenutt, G. W. 1929. The Cliff-founder and Landslide at Gore Cliff, Isle of Wight. *Proc. Isle Wight nat. Hist. archaeol. Soc.* (for 1928). 1(9):561-570.

Collins, K. J., Herbert, R. J. H. & Mallinson, J. M. 1990. The Marine Flora and Fauna of Bembridge and St. Helens, Isle of Wight. *Proc. Isle Wight nat. Hist. archaeol. Soc.* (for 1989). 9: 41-85.

Daley, B. & Insole, A. 1984. The Isle of Wight – No. 25. *Geologists' Association Guides*. London.

Donisthorpe, St. J. K. 1909. Supplementary List of *Coleoptera* in Morey's *Guide to the Natural History of the Isle of Wight*. Isle of Wight County Press.

Dony, J. G., Rob. C. M. & Perring, F. H. 1974. *English Names of Wild Flowers*. Butterworths for B.S.B.I.

Dover, J. 1909. Meteorology in Morey's *Guide to the Natural History of the Isle of Wight*. Isle of Wight County Press.

Falconer, W. 1931. Isle of Wight *Arachnida*. *Proc. Isle Wight nat. Hist. archaeol. Soc.* (for 1931). 2(2): 118-124.

Farnham, W. F. 1982. *Species List of the Benthic Algae of the Isle of Wight*. Report to the D. of E.

Ford, R. L. E. 1983. Black Rats at Yarmouth. *Proc. Isle Wight nat. Hist. archaeol. Soc.* (for 1982). 7(7): 523-524.

Fox, R. H. 1909. List of Birds in Morey's *Guide to the Natural*

History of the Isle of Wight. Isle of Wight County Press.

Frazer, J. F. D. 1973. *Amphibians*. Wykeham Series.

Frazer, D. 1983. *Reptiles and Amphibians in Britain*. Collins New Naturalist.

Frazer, O. H. 1965. A Survey of the Frog and Toad Spawning Areas in the Isle of Wight – 1964. *Proc. Isle Wight nat. Hist. archaeol. Soc.* (for 1964). 5(9): 397-403.

Frazer, O. H. 1966. Investigation into the Distribution of Newts in the Isle of Wight in 1965. *Proc. Isle Wight nat. Hist. archaeol. Soc.* (for 1965). 5(10): 454-457.

Frazer, O. H. 1967. Second Survey of the Frog and Toad Spawning Areas. *Proc. Isle Wight nat. Hist. archaeol. Soc.* (for 1966). 6(1): 49-55.

Frazer, O. H. 1969. Third Survey of the Frog and Toad Spawning Areas. *Proc. Isle Wight nat. Hist. archaeol. Soc.* (for 1968). 6(3): 189-194.

Frazer, O. H. 1970. Survey of the Distribution of the Land Mammals in the I.W. *Proc. Isle Wight nat. Hist. archaeol. Soc.* (for 1969). 6(4): 233-236.

Frazer, O. H. 1971. Fourth Survey of the Frog and Toad Spawning Areas. *Proc. Isle Wight nat. Hist. archaeol. Soc.* (for 1970). 6(5): 337-344.

Frazer, O. H. 1976. Fifth Survey of the Frog and Toad Spawning Areas. *Proc. Isle Wight nat. Hist. archaeol. Soc.* (for 1975). 6(10): 654-660.

Frazer, O. H. 1977. Survey of Newts in the Isle of Wight. *Proc. Isle Wight nat. Hist. archaeol. Soc.* (for 1976). 7(1): 33-38.

Frazer, O. H. 1981. Sixth Survey of the Frog and Toad Spawning Areas. *Proc. Isle Wight nat. Hist. archaeol. Soc.* (for 1980). 7(5): 341-351.

Frazer, O. H. 1988a. National Small Mammal Survey at Walter's Copse, Newton, Isle of Wight, 1983-1986. *Proc. Isle Wight nat. Hist. archaeol. Soc.* (for 1987). 8(2): 45-60.

Frazer, O. H. 1988b. Bechstein's Bat in the Isle of Wight. *Proc. Isle Wight nat. Hist. archaeol. Soc.* (for 1987). 8(2): 63-65.

Frazer, O. H. 1990. The History of Marine Mammals off the Isle of Wight. *Proc. Isle Wight nat. Hist. archaeol. Soc.* (for 1989). 9: 17-32.

Goater, B. 1974. *The Butterflies and Moths of Hampshire and the Isle of Wight*. E. W. Classey.

Groves, J. 1928. The Story of our *Spartina*. *Proc. Isle Wight nat. Hist. archaeol. Soc.* (for 1927). 2(8): 509-513.

Gunn, J. 1972. Badgers in General. *Proc. Isle Wight nat. Hist. archaeol. Soc.* (for 1971). 6(6): 413-416.

Herbert, R. J. H. 1988. Marine Biological Recorder's Report 1986. *Proc. Isle Wight nat. Hist. archaeol. Soc.* (for 1987). 8(2):66-67.

Herbert, R. J. H. 1989a. A Survey of the Dog-whelk *Nucella lapillus* (L.) around the Coast of the Isle of Wight. *Proc. Isle Wight nat. Hist. archaeol. Soc.* (for 1988). 8(3): 15-21.

Herbert, R. J. H. 1989b. Isle of Wight Marine Biological Report for 1987. *Proc. Isle Wight nat. Hist. archaeol. Soc.* (for 1988). 8(3): 37-42.

Herbert, R. J. H. 1990. Isle of Wight Marine Biological Report for 1988. *Proc. Isle Wight nat. Hist. archaeol. Soc.* (for 1989).

9: 15-16.

Hockey, S. F. 1982. *Insula vecta*. Phillimore.

Holm, J. 1987. *Squirrels*. Whittet.

Holm, J. 1989. *The Red Squirrel*. Shire Natural History Series.

Hutchinson, L. 1969. *Botany, Birds, Bugs and Barrows of the Isle of Wight* (the Jubilee History of the Society). Isle of Wight County Press.

Hutt, S., Simmons, K. and Hullman, G. 1990. Predatory Dinosaurs of the Isle of Wight. *Proc. Isle Wight nat. Hist. archaeol. Soc.* (for 1989). 9: 137-146.

Insole, A. N. & Daley, B. 1985. A Revision of the Lithostratigraphical Nomenclature of the Late Eocene and Early Oligocene Strata of the Hampshire Basin, Southern England. *Tertiary Res.* 7: 67-100.

Jarzembowski, E. A. 1980. Fossil Insects from the Lower Hamsteads Beds (lower oligocene) of the Isle of Wight. *Proc. Isle Wight nat. Hist. archaeol. Soc.* (for 1978). 7(3): 167-170.

Jeffery, H. G. 1929. A Supplementary List of Isle of Wight *Lepidoptera*. *Proc. Isle Wight nat. Hist. archaeol. Soc.* (for 1928). 1(9): 584-598.

Jeffery, H. G. 1931. The Formicidae (or Ants) of the Isle of Wight. *Proc. Isle Wight nat. Hist. archaeol. Soc.* (for 1931). 2(2): 125-128.

Jones, D. 1985. Analysis of Owl's Pellets from Rock Roman Villa, compared with modern samples (unpublished).

Jones, J. & J. 1987. *The Isle of Wight*. Dovecote Press.

Keay, A. N. 1980. Centipedes in the Isle of Wight. *Proc. Isle Wight nat. Hist. archaeol. Soc.* (for 1978). 7(3): 194-196.

Keay, A. N. 1988. *Trachysphaera lobata* Ribaut, a Millipede New to Britain, in the Isle of Wight. *Proc. Isle Wight nat. Hist. archaeol. Soc.* (for 1987). 8(2): 43-44.

Kersall & Munn, P. W. 1905. *The Birds of Hampshire and the Isle of Wight*.

Kerney, M. P. 1976. *Atlas of the Non-marine Molluscs of the British Isles*. I.T.E. Cambridge.

Kerney, M. P. & Cameron, R. A. D. 1979. *A Field Guide to the Land Snails of Britain and Northwest Europe*. Collins.

Leighton, D. 1909. List of *Polyzoa* in Morey's *Guide to the Natural History of the Isle of Wight*. Isle of Wight County Press.

Lever, C. 1977. *The Naturalized Animals of the British Isles*. Hutchinson.

Light, J. & Killeen, I. 1990. A Survey to Record the Marine *Mollusca* of the Isle of Wight. *Proc. Isle Wight nat. Hist. archaeol. Soc.* (for 1989). 9: 86-90.

Livens, H. M. 1909. List of Mosses in Morey's *Guide to the Natural History of the Isle of Wight*. Isle of Wight County Press.

Livens, H. M. 1927a. Hepatics (supplementary list). *Proc. Isle Wight nat. Hist. archaeol. Soc.* (for 1926). 1(7): 452-453.

Livens, H. M. 1927b. Mosses (supplementary list). *Proc. Isle Wight nat. Hist. archaeol. Soc.* (for 1926). 1(7): 454-457.

Lousley, J. E. 1969. *Wild Flowers of Chalk and Limestone*. Ed. 2. Collins New Naturalist.

Lucas, C .C. 1972. Report on Pleistocene Deposits in Newtown Reserve. *Proc. Isle Wight nat. Hist. archaeol. Soc.* (for

1971). 6(6): 401-404.

Lucas, W. J. 1909. List of *Neuroptera* in Morey's *Guide to the Natural History of the Isle of Wight*. Isle of Wight County Press.

Meade-Waldo, 1900. List of Birds in the *Victoria History of Hampshire and the Isle of Wight*.

Millidge, A. F. 1959. Spiders. *Proc. Isle Wight nat. Hist. archaeol. Soc.* (for 1958). 5(3): 102-108.

More, A. G. 1860. List of Birds in Venable's *Guide to the Isle of Wight*.

More, A. G. 1872. Supplement to the *Flora Vectensis* in *Journ. Bot. 9*.

Morey, F. 1909. *A Guide to the Natural History of the Isle of Wight*. Isle of Wight County Press.

Morley, C. 1909. List of *Hymenoptera* in Morey's *Guide to the Natural History of the Isle of Wight*. Isle of Wight County Press.

Morris, Dr P. A. 1988. *The Hedgehog*. Shire Natural History Series.

Munt, M. C. & Burke, A. 1987. The Pleistocene Geology and Faunas at Newtown, Isle of Wight. *Proc. Isle Wight nat. Hist. archaeol. Soc.* (for 1986). 8(1): 7-14.

Newberry, E. A. 1909. List of Coleoptera in Morey's *Guide to the Natural History of the Isle of Wight*. Isle of Wight County Press.

O'Brien, C. & Parkinson, C. 1881. *Wild Flowers of the Undercliff*. Reeve.

Page (ed). 1900. *The Victoria History of Hampshire and the Isle of Wight*.

Parker, M. J. 1990. The Distribution and Populatiopns of Bats in Cowes, 1985-1988. *Proc. Isle Wight nat. Hist. archaeol. Soc.* (for 1989). 9: 151-160.

Pinder, R. 1972. Badgers in Particular. *Proc. Isle Wight nat. Hist. archaeol. Soc.* (for 1971). 6(6): 416-418.

Poole, H. F. 1909. List of *Lepidoptera* in Morey's *Guide to the Natural History of the Isle of Wight*. Isle of Wight County Press.

Poole, H. F. 1922. Additions to the List of Isle of Wight *Lepidoptera*. *Proc. Isle Wight nat. Hist. archaeol. Soc.* (for 1921). 1(2): 81-83.

Poole, H. F. 1934. Belgic Cooking Pot from Lake, Sandown. *Proc. Isle Wight nat. Hist. archaeol. Soc.* (for 1933). 2(4): 324-325.

Pope, C. R. 1974. Some Aspects of Lichen Distribution. *Proc. Isle Wight nat. Hist. archaeol. Soc.* (for 1973). 6(8): 536-541.

Pope, C. R. 1977. Notes on the Lichens of the Isle of Wight. *Proc. Isle Wight nat. Hist. archaeol. Soc.* (for 1976). 7(1): 39-42.

Pope, C. R. 1985. A Lichen Flora of the Isle of Wight. *Proc. Isle Wight nat. Hist. archaeol. Soc.* (for 1983). 7(8): 571-599.

Pope, C. R. 1988. The Status of the Glanville Fritillary on the Isle of Wight. *Proc. Isle Wight nat. Hist. archaeol. Soc.* (for 1987). 8(2): 33-42.

Pope, C. R. 1990. The Historic Flora of Ryde Dover. *Proc. Isle Wight nat. Hist. archaeol. Soc.* (for 1989). 9: 33-40.

Preece, R. C. 1976. The Non-marine *Mollusca* of the Isle of Wight. *Proc. Isle Wight nat. Hist. archaeol. Soc.* (for 1975).

6(10): 647-651.

Preece, R. C. 1980a. *An Atlas of the Non-marine Mollusca of the Isle of Wight*. I.W. County Museum Service. Natural History Series No. 1.

Preece, R. C. 1980b. The Biostratigraphy and Dating of a Post-glacial Slope Deposit at Gore Cliff, near Blackgang, Isle of Wight. *Journal of Archaeological Science*. 7: 255-265.

Preece, R. C. 1982. *Pisidium pulchellum* Jenyns in the Isle of Wight. *Proc. Isle Wight nat. Hist. archaeol. Soc.* (for 1980). 7(5): 339.

Preece, R. C. 1984. *Boettgerilla pallens* Simroth, a New Slug to the Isle of Wight. *Proc. Isle Wight nat. Hist. archaeol. Soc.* (for 1982). 7(7):488.

Preece, R. C. 1986. Faunal Remains from Radiocarbon-dated Soils within Landslip Debris from the Undercliff, Isle of Wight. *Journal of Archaeological Science*. 13: 189-200.

Pring, S. W. 1909. List of *Infusoria* in Morey's *Guide to the Natural History of the Isle of Wight*. Isle of Wight County Press.

Pring, S. W. & Walker, F. M. 1909. List of *Rotifera* in Morey's *Guide to the Natural History of the Isle of Wight*. Isle of Wight County Press.

Ragge, D. R. 1973. The British Orthoptera – a Supplement. *Entomological Gazette*. 24(3): 227-245.

Rayner, J. F. 1909. List of *Fungi* in Morey's *Guide to the Natural History of the Isle of Wight*. Isle of Wight County Press.

Rayner, J. F. 1925. A List of the Alien Plants of Hampshire and the Isle of Wight. *Proc. Isle Wight nat. Hist. archaeol. Soc.* (for 1924). 1(5): 229-274.

Rayner J. F. 1929. Supplement to Townsend's *Flora of Hampshire, including the Isle of Wight*.

Rose, F. 1981. *The Wild Flower Key*. Warne.

Rose, F. 1989. *Colour Identification Guide to the Grasses, Sedges, Rushes and Ferns of the British Isles*. Viking.

Scott, S. 1984. Changes in Natural and Semi-natural Vegetation in the Isle of Wight since the 1850's. *Proc. Isle Wight nat. Hist. archaeol. Soc.* (for 1982). 7(7): 497-517.

Shepard, B. 1970. Bleak Down. *Proc. Isle Wight nat. Hist. archaeol. Soc.* (for 1969). 6(4): 231-232.

Shepard, B. 1971. St. Helens Duver. *Proc. Isle Wight nat. Hist. archaeol. Soc.* (for 1970). 6(5):320-328.

Shepard, B. 1972. Island Orchids. *Proc. Isle Wight nat. Hist. archaeol. Soc.* (for 1971). 6(6): 405-413.

Shepard, B. 1973. Island Ferns and Fern Allies. *Proc. Isle Wight nat. Hist. archaeol. Soc.* (for 1972). 6(7): 489-492.

Shepard, B. 1976. Our Disappearing Elms – a Naturalist's View. *Proc. Isle Wight nat. Hist. archaeol. Soc.* (for 1975). 6(10): 640-641.

Shepard, B. *et al.* 1978. Habitat Studies No. 1 The Flora of the River Medina. *Proc. Isle Wight nat. Hist. archaeol. Soc.* (for 1977). 7(2): 101-106.

Shepard, B. *et al.* 1979. Habitat Studies No. 2 Woodland. *Proc. Isle Wight nat. Hist. archaeol. Soc.* (for 1978). 7(3): 189-193.

Shepard, B. *et al.* 1981a. Interpreting the Countryside. *Proc. Isle Wight nat. Hist. archaeol. Soc.* (for 1980). 7(5): 308-316.

Shepard, B. *et al.* 1981b. Habitat Studies No. 3 The Eastern

Yar. *Proc. Isle Wight nat. Hist. archaeol. Soc.* (for 1980). 7(5): 317-324.

Shepard, B. 1984. A Supplement to the Flora of the Isle of Wight, 1978. *Proc. Isle Wight nat. Hist. archaeol. Soc.* (for 1983). 7(8): 569-576.

Smith, C. J. 1980. *Ecology of the English Chalk.* Academic Press.

Smith, F. P. 1909. List of *Arachnida* in Morey's *Guide to the Natural History of the Isle of Wight.* Isle of Wight County Press.

Snooke, W. D. 1823. *Flora Vectiana.* Taylor.

Snow, L. 1979. Rediscovery of Rare Moss *Philonotis marchica* (Hedw) Brid. at Shanklin, Isle of Wight. *Proc. Isle Wight nat. Hist. archaeol. Soc.* (for 1977). 7(2): 107-108.

Snow, L. 1990. Provisional Atlas of the Bryophytes of the Isle of Wight – Liverworts. *Proc. Isle Wight nat. Hist. archaeol. Soc.* (for 1989). 9: 121-134.

Stafford, J. 1953-1983. Annual Bird Reports. *Proc. Isle Wight nat. Hist. archaeol. Soc.*

Stafford, J. 1984- . *Isle of Wight Birds,* including Annual Bird Report.

Stratton, F. 1909. Flowering Plants and their Allies in Morey's *Guide to the Natural History of the Isle of Wight.* Isle of Wight County Press.

Swanton, E. W. 1935. List of *Fungi* found in the Isle of Wight. *Proc. Isle Wight nat. Hist. archaeol. Soc.* (for 1934). 2(5): 365-394.

Swanton, E. W. 1938. A Preliminary Annotated List of Plant Galls Observed in The Isle of Wight. *Proc. Isle Wight nat. Hist. archaeol. Soc.* (for 1937). 2(8): 654-669.

Townsend, F. 1883. *Flora of Hampshire, including the Isle of Wight.* Reeve.

Venables, E. 1860. *A Guide to the Isle of Wight.*

Wadham, P. 1909. Notes on Fish, Amphibians, Reptiles and Mammals in Morey's *Guide to the Natural History of the Isle of Wight.* Isle of Wight County Press.

Wadham, P. 1937. Notes on the Fish, Reptiles and Mammals

of the Isle of Wight. *Proc. Isle Wight nat. Hist. archaeol. Soc.* (for 1936). 2(7): 598-601.

Wadham, P. 1943. The Black or Ship Rat. *Proc. Isle Wight nat. Hist. archaeol. Soc.* (for 1942). 3(5): 345.

Waring, P. 1990. 1988 Survey of the Reddish Buff Moth, *Acosmetia caliginsa,* on the Isle of Wight. *Proc. Isle Wight nat. Hist. archaeol. Soc.* (for 1989). 9: 147-150.

Warner, R. 1975. *The History of the Isle of Wight.*

West, G. S. 1909. List of Freshwater *Algae* in Morey's *Guide to the Natural History of the Isle of Wight.* Isle of Wight County Press.

Wheldon, G. S. 1909. List of Lichens in Morey's *Guide to the Natural History of the Isle of Wight.* Isle of Wight County Press.

White, H. J. O. 1921. A Short Account of the Geology of the Isle of Wight. *Mem. geol. Survey G.B.* (Reprinted 1968).

Wilkinson, A. 1980. Harvest Mouse at Niton. *Proc. Isle Wight nat. Hist. archaeol. Soc.* (for 1979). 7(4): 268.

Withers, R. G. 1979a. The Marine Macrofauna and Flora of the Medina Estuary. *Proc. Isle Wight nat. Hist. archaeol. Soc.* (for 1976). 7(1): 19-30.

Withers, R. G. 1979b. Observations of the Macrofauna of Intertidal Sands at Ryde and Bembridge, Isle of Wight. *Proc. Isle Wight nat. Hist. archaeol. Soc.* (for 1977). 7(2): 81-89.

Worsley, R. 1781. *History of the Isle of Wight.* London.

In addition to the above there are many natural history books available, of which the following are especially recommended:

Collins Field and Pocket Guides

Hamlyn Guides

Hulton Group Keys

Shire Natural History Series

Warne's Wayside and Woodland Series

Whittet Natural History Series

Index